GHOSTS IN
THE HEDGEROW

A Hedgehog Whodunnit

Tom Moorhouse

doubleday

TRANSWORLD PUBLISHERS

Penguin Random House, One Embassy Gardens,
8 Viaduct Gardens, London SW11 7BW
www.penguin.co.uk

Transworld is part of the Penguin Random House group of companies
whose addresses can be found at global.penguinrandomhouse.com

First published in Great Britain in 2023 by Doubleday
an imprint of Transworld Publishers

Copyright © Tom Moorhouse 2023

Tom Moorhouse has asserted his right under the Copyright,
Designs and Patents Act 1988 to be identified as the author of this work.

Epigraph on p. 14 from *Death Proof* written by Quentin Tarantino.

Every effort has been made to obtain the necessary permissions with
reference to copyright material, both illustrative and quoted. We apologize
for any omissions in this respect and will be pleased to make the
appropriate acknowledgements in any future edition.

A CIP catalogue record for this book
is available from the British Library.

ISBN 9780857528445

Typeset in 11/19 pt ITC Berkeley Oldstyle Pro by Jouve (UK), Milton Keynes
Printed and bound in Great Britain by Clays Ltd, Elcograf S.p.A.

The authorized representative in the EEA is Penguin Random House Ireland,
Morrison Chambers, 32 Nassau Street, Dublin D02 YH68.

Penguin Random House is committed to a sustainable future
for our business, our readers and our planet. This book is made
from Forest Stewardship Council® certified paper.

To my beautiful Ellie, hoping that one day she'll meet a hedgehog.

CONTENTS

CHAPTER 1

Murder Most Horrid

The game is afoot.

ARTHUR CONAN DOYLE,
The Return of Sherlock Holmes

THE GUESTS ASSEMBLE IN THE LIBRARY OF HOTEL FURZEHOGE. They whisper in groups and cast glances over to where the Detective and her officers are conferring.

The Detective turns to them, her expression stern. 'Ladies and gentlemen, my apologies for drawing you from your evening's entertainment. But be assured this is a matter of the gravest urgency. I regret to inform you' – and here her gaze sweeps the guests – 'that there has been a murder.'

Shock ripples through the room.

'A murder', the Detective continues, 'that forms part of a despicable series of wildlife killings. And what is more, the perpetrator is among us, here in this very library.'

At that the gathering goes silent.

'That's right, ladies and gentlemen. So we've barred the doors. Nobody is to pass in or out until our killer has been identified, and their motives uncovered.' She grins at the guests' consternation. 'This promises to be quite a night.'

3

'A murderer?' says a man in tweeds. 'Here? One of us?' He huffs and says, 'Preposterous.'

'Interesting that you should say that . . . Major Geddoff, isn't it?' The Detective flips open her notebook and scribbles for a moment. Major Geddoff hastily seats himself. 'And as for "preposterous", well, don't take my word for it. See for yourselves.'

The Detective draws back the curtains. Everyone cranes for a view. The grounds of Hotel Furzehoge are buzzing with boiler-suited officers. The croquet lawn is cordoned off. Its cropped grass now bears a stark, white outline – a rough oblong, with a snouty shape for a head. And before anyone can speak, a trolley is wheeled past. The body it bears is respectfully covered, but spines poke out here and there through the sheet. And when the trolley jars against the sill of the police van, a spindly leg slips into view. The trolley is hastily stowed and the van doors slammed shut. But the image of the leg is indelible: a hairy, wrinkly appendage, ending in four elongated toes.*

The Detective watches the van drive off. 'Far from preposterous, I think you'll agree. Deadly serious, in fact.' Her voice is soft. 'So, before we get started, does anyone have anything to say to me?' She

---

* The game is a foot! (I'm only slightly ashamed of this pun.)

4

folds her arms. 'Anything on the subject of who could possibly have it in for all these poor hedgehogs?'

It's a very good question. I mean, really, who could? Because I have never met anyone who doesn't love hedgehogs. I can think of literally nobody who wouldn't be delighted to see one bumbling down a hedgerow or ambling into their garden. Oh, I'm sure there exist a scattering of hog-aversive types who wouldn't bother to rush out with a plate of food and a smart-phone in the hope of recording something wonderful. But I'm equally sure that those folks – who must have their reasons – are very much in the minority. And I can support this assertion with statistics. Hedgehogs are unquestionably Britain's favourite mammal. In 2016 they won a national poll, with a whopping 35.9 per cent of the vote. My own beloved 'Ratty' (the water vole) didn't get so much as a sniff, with a measly 3.6 per cent.* And even in the face of such a comprehensive defeat I can't

---

* This put water voles behind foxes, red squirrels, wild cats, otters and pine martens, in joint seventh place with – of all things – soprano pipistrelle bats. I cannot begin to fathom how Kenneth Graham's 'Ratty' ended up sharing his level of popularity with what is essentially a hang-gliding shrew. Don't get me wrong, bats are wonderful, but they don't exactly radiate charisma.

bring myself to be bitter about it because *of course* hedgehogs were the winners. They were bound to be. Just look at them! Look at the way they walk, like sweetly determined toddlers, and the snuffling noises they make when they're doing it! No other mammal inspires such devotion, and no other is so lovably able to be approached and picked up,* marvelled at, fed and then watched pootling amiably away to do you a favour by feasting on your garden's slug and snail population. And so it is both alarming and perplexing to read reports of the increasingly drastic national decline in their numbers.

The details from the police files provide few initial hints as to the causes. The notes describe an indigenous, insectivorous† adult mammal, typically expected to live for seven to ten years. She was of no fixed abode. In the summer she distributed her time among a large number of well-appointed

---

* Please don't, though. Remember these are wild animals. They won't necessarily see the funny side of being grabbed and waved about for someone's amusement while they're busily trying to eat enough to survive.

† Actually, while they do mainly eat invertebrates, they are happy to take in other sources of animal protein and also some plants. So they're firmly on the omnivorous side of insectivory.

leafy nests in various sheltered spots, notably in hedgerows. In the winter she traded these for an exclusive 'hibernaculum', a larger nest sunk partially into the ground, among tree roots, bramble branches or other supportive structures, and lined with a 20cm thick layer of dead leaves – all laminated together against the cold. She was known for an endearingly gruff attitude, solitary tendencies and a dislike of being called 'Tiggy-Winkle'. And for the last ten thousand years at least, that's how her kind have lived in Britain. The lifestyle worked. It made hedgehogs a notable success.

But these days hedgehogs aren't so successful. A quick internet search will bag you article after article – from national newspapers to the blogs of popular TV shows and wildlife specialists – depicting a country haemorrhaging hedgehogs. They all agree on the details: in the 1950s their numbers were estimated at thirty-six million; since then, they have dropped to little more than half a million. And the rate of decrease shows little sign of abating. Numbers are estimated to have halved between 2000 and 2018. And this, remember, is a species that *really counts* with the public. You might be forgiven for not having noticed that the lesser self-effacing innocuous sorry-to-bother-you beetle has silently vanished from the one patch of remote moorland it inhabited. But hedgehogs come into our gardens, often nightly. If we can't save them from disaster, then surely the rest of our wildlife is doomed.

But never fear, I hear you cry, the hedgehog's plight has not gone unnoticed! Indeed, in January 2021 the UK press trumpeted the intention of one of Britain's senior politicians to 'lead the charge' to save them. This certainly sounded encouraging. The 'charge' in question comprised a campaign for legal protection of hedgehogs' nesting sites. Such protection is long overdue, and would form a vital part of future conservation efforts, especially helpful in preventing new housing developments from ignoring the presence of nesting hedgehogs and doing, in essence, whatever they want. And look, any fleeting political goodwill directed towards wildlife is something to be cherished. But not to sound curmudgeonly about the extent of the benefits anticipated from the campaign, nothing, at the time of writing, has actually changed.* And beyond that, the underlying implication of 'the charge to save them' is that this single intervention could reverse the hedgehog's fortunes. That would be optimistic. At worst, it risks people thinking that it will solve everything by itself: change that legislation, job done, nice charge everyone, thanks for your support.

---

* So not, perhaps, a charge. More of a casual saunter.

So if, like me, your response to this news was, 'Well, it's good but sounds deceptively simple,' then you might be on to something. Because, you will recall, we have a library full of murder suspects awaiting investigation. And there are multiple suspects for a good reason: that even after decades of research, many causes of the hedgehog's decline are still subject to investigation and debate, as are the best solutions to those causes. And if any charge to their rescue is to be even fractionally more successful than some other famous charges in history,* said enterprise must be well informed, tightly conceived, adequately funded, universally adopted by all the key stakeholders and (quite important, this) likely actually to arrive somewhere at some point.

Protecting nesting sites is an excellent first step. But that's all it is: a first step. Any plan to return hedgehog populations to full strength will have to be intricate and careful, and based on a nuanced understanding of the ills that are befalling them.

---

* With apologies to Tennyson: 'Half a step, half a step, Half a step forward, All in the valley of Death, Rode the bewildered . . . Not tho' the hedgehog knew, Someone had blundered: Theirs not to make reply, Theirs not to reason why, Theirs but to do and continue to die at a higher rate than will be sustainable for their populations in the long term.' I won't go on.

Acting appropriately upon such an understanding is surely the only way any species can be set upon the path to conservation recovery. And the best way of deriving that understanding is to subject the likely suspects to forensic scrutiny.

Which brings us to the matter at hand: that somewhere in the lamplit library of Hotel Furzehoge sits a killer. Their expression is innocent, but they cannot hide for ever. The game is afoot, the hunt is upon us, and the *Case of the Disappearing Hedgehogs* is itching to be opened.* Will our mystery unfurl like a deftly plotted Agatha Christie novel, with every detail and red herring scrupulously considered? Or do we face some ramshackle tale of the unexpected, all implausible twists and drama aplenty? Shall we uncover a nefarious hedgehog death cult? Is it a lone-wolf hedgehog assassin, out for vengeance? Or perhaps we could take an even darker path. We might, like protagonists in a Scandi-noir dystopian fiction, uncover lingering and uncomfortable truths about our friends, families and neighbours. Perhaps our findings will strike closer to our homes and hearts than we could have imagined.

Who knows? At this moment I certainly cannot tell you.

---

* If this left you with a mental image of a case full of itching hedgehogs, my sincerest apologies.

The three years of my conservation research career I spent entangled with hedgehogs have furnished me in advance with the wherewithal to populate our hotel library. They have provided a full cast of characters, and the first guesses at their motivations. But as I sit down to write it is with the suspicion that the unfolding of this spiny tale may yet hold surprises for all of us.

So let us don our extravagant moustaches, our deerstalkers, our ferocious-yet-disarmingly-sweet-lady-of-indeterminate-age-appropriate sensible shoes (or whatever accoutrements best embody the idiosyncratic sartorial choices of your favoured deliverer of detecting derring-do), and let us sharpen our deductive faculties, set aside our preconceptions and prepare to sleuth our way to the solution of our very own murder mystery!

The suspects are assembled. The stakes could not be higher. The task that befalls us is nothing less than the prevention of murder, the saving of a species, and the bringing of those responsible to justice* . . .

---

* Given the typical outcome of wildlife prosecutions in Britain, 'justice' may amount merely to waggling an admonishing finger until they say sorry. But at least we'll know who to waggle it at.

*

The guests avoid one another's gazes. The Detective's face is impassive. Somebody will crack, they always do. But who will be first to break their silence?

In the end Ms Nymbies, local parishioner, clears her throat. She raises her voice to say what she suspects should be on everybody's mind – which is, and she's so terribly sorry to have to mention this, that the killer of course must be Mr Clarkson, the chauffeur. Nothing personal, naturally, Mr Clarkson, but surely everyone has seen the unforgivable mess his vehicles leave lying at the side of our carriageways. What more evidence would one need? The poor little mites never stood a chance, did they?

CHAPTER 2

Driven to Destruction

This car is 100% death proof. Only to get the benefit of it . . . you *really* need to be sitting in my seat.

STUNTMAN MIKE
Death Proof

LET'S START WITH THE OBVIOUS. HEDGEHOGS GET RUN over. A lot. Hence the plethora of jokes, which I will refrain from repeating.* And you'd have to imagine that the sheer quantity of vehicularly mediated hedgehog-enflattenings would leave a fairly substantial dent in their populations (and, of course, extremely substantial dents in individual hedge-hogs). A cursory glance at the national hedgehog and traffic statistics certainly appears to bear this out.

In 1950 there were four million vehicles on British roads, and an estimated thirty-six million hedgehogs snuffling about. Since then the fortunes of cars and hedgehogs have diverged in a suspiciously inversely correlated fashion.

---

* I've noticed that the quantity of 'Why did the hedgehog . . . ?' jokes in my own social environment has decreased dramatically over the last thirty years or so. Is this because those jokes aren't very funny, or because they only really get told to children, or because people have noticed the sad trend in actual hedgehog numbers?

Traffic has surged year on year: twenty million vehicles in the 1980s, twenty-seven million by 2000 and almost thirty-three million in 2020. Meanwhile, estimates of the national hedgehog population plummeted to 1,550,000 in 1995, and further to a measly 550,000 in 2018, our most recent estimate. The estimates indicate a 98 per cent decline in hedgehogs in four decades, during which traffic increased sixfold.

Scarier still are the numbers of hedgehogs engaging in sadly one-sided altercations with motor vehicles. Recent estimates suggest that in 1993 we may have had 230,000 hedgehog road deaths. Taking the closest population estimate (from 1995), that approximates to 15 per cent of all the hedgehogs alive at the time. The road-death estimate for 2016 was between 167,000 and 335,000. In the context of the nearest population estimate (from 2018), that equates to 30–60 per cent of all British hedgehogs in existence. To put it another way, the 1993 and 2016 estimates of hedgehog road deaths are similarly and brutally high, but the context of those deaths has changed markedly. National population estimates suggest that we lost around 39 per cent of our hedgehogs between 1995 and 2018. So the recent deaths are drawn from a far smaller population.

The revealed trend is of ever-increasing car numbers resulting in ever-increasing percentages of an ever-decreasing national hedgehog population being wiped out on the road. And now, every year, cars kill hedgehogs in quantities that veer perilously close to the sum total of all the British hedgehogs alive.

So I'm afraid this is going to be a rather short book. Even the most optimistic defence lawyer would agree that these facts don't look great for our chauffeur. The casualties are appalling. Any protestations Mr Clarkson might attempt must surely be pointless.

And they *would* be pointless, if the statistics I've just cited constituted a reliable basis from which to draw conclusions. But, like any good detective, we should examine our sources. The vehicle statistics came from the government, so I assume they are relatively accurate. The hedgehog estimates are all from academic studies and scientific reports, compiled by diligent, respected researchers who are experts in hedgehog and mammalian ecology. Those researchers all did their jobs absolutely correctly. And their findings, remember, have been cited by a wide variety of prestigious national newspapers, online news outlets, wildlife bodies and TV programmes. So the hedgehog stats must also be robust. Right?

No. I'm sorry, but really not.* Like most people, my reaction to a solid number is initially to assume that it is based on good evidence, and that people using that number have done their due diligence. So when I read that in the 1950s British hedgehogs numbered approximately thirty-six million, I assumed that someone had gone out surveying in some systematic fashion. But the reality is that no organizations or individuals in the 1950s were out counting hedgehogs on a national basis.[†] There *still* isn't an organization out surveying live hedgehogs on a national basis now. Which leads to the obvious question of where that statistic could have come from.

The lamentably-still-quoted thirty-six million estimate

---

* This book is a murder mystery. Nobody would settle down for a nice Agatha without expecting the occasional red herring. And the national population estimates comprise a particularly pungent example of the crimson piscine oeuvre. A 98% decline indeed! Can't believe you – and nearly everyone else, including me before I looked into it – fell for that.

† I have said before, in my book *Elegy for a River* (Doubleday, 2021), that before the Mammal Society was formed in 1965 the only people systematically recording numbers of mammals in Britain were basically trying to string them up, shoot them or otherwise exterminate them in a variety of inventive ways. But at least they kept records.

originates in a rather lovely book from 1969 entitled *The Hedgehog*. Its author, Maurice Burton, makes detailed observations about hedgehog behaviour and ecology, while also outlining some threats to their populations. In addition to these, at the top of page 119, he writes:

> In the 1950s I ventured an estimate of the size of the average density [of hedgehogs] throughout this country as one per acre. A survey by Zimmerman in Germany in the 1930s gave an average of 1 hedgehog per 25 acres. This disparity merely emphasizes the difficulty of making an accurate count.

That, believe it or not, is the sum total of information underpinning the 1950s population estimate. Of course, Burton's hedgehog density needed to be translated into a national figure. Multiplying one hedgehog per acre across all of the non-urban habitats in Great Britain, excluding the uplands where hedgehogs are scarce, does indeed yield 36,500,000 hedgehogs. The study that produced this figure in 1995 definitely did not suggest it was remotely reliable, stating that Burton's 1969 hedgehog density estimate was 'derived largely from guesswork'. But to understand just how *much* guesswork was involved, we must turn to the undisputed British heavyweight champion of hedgehog research, Dr Pat Morris. In his 2018 book *Hedgehog*,* Pat reveals that when he asked Burton about the density estimate, 'he told me that it was based on seeing about ten hedgehogs in ten acres during an evening's stroll in Kew Gardens'.

An evening's stroll does not constitute an entirely credible basis for a national population estimate. If Burton hadn't seen any hedgehogs, we wouldn't conclude that there were none to be found across the whole of Britain. And if he had seen one hedgehog, nobody would multiply that up to a whopping 3.7 million of them. And since we can't assume that Burton was able to count all of the hedgehogs living in the area, or that he surveyed exactly 10 acres, the scaled-up estimate could be out by multiple tens of millions. Many other assumptions

---

* The titles of hedgehog books do tend towards the literal. But that's about the only criticism anyone could level at Pat Morris's contribution to hedgehogdom. His name will crop up a lot in the coming pages, simply because he has been so influential for such a long time. He is the president of the British Hedgehog Preservation Society and in the words of more than one of the other researchers I spoke to, the doyen of UK hedgehog research. Pat was the world's first hedgehog PhD, has received an MBE for his work, and is routinely frustrated by people coming along and trying to repeat stuff he knows is already done and proven – the curse of any highly successful ecologist.

underlying this estimate are equally dodgy. We would need to assume, for instance, that the whole of the rest of lowland rural Britain is just as good for hedgehogs as Kew Gardens. Spoiler alert – it's not. In the words of one prominent hedgehog researcher, the 1950s national hedgehog population estimate is 'a nonsense' – and, moreover, a nonsense to which Burton apparently had no intention of contributing, given that he used his figures to highlight the difficulty of making an accurate count.

But once anyone derives a figure, even if they unequivocally state that it is based on guesswork, that figure is liable to be picked up and used. The thirty-six million was only ever intended as a brief nod to some historical context, not to be taken seriously. There probably weren't thirty-six million hedgehogs in Britain in the 1950s. Or conceivably there were, but we simply can't know. And we must now make our peace with that, and forget that the estimate exists.

The first semi-credible estimate of national hedgehog numbers is from 1995, derived as part of a wider exercise assessing the state of British mammal populations. The authors took published measures of hedgehog density in different habitats (e.g. woodlands, lowland grasslands, scrublands, parklands, amenity areas, built-up areas, arable fields etc.), and multiplied them by the amount of that habitat in Britain. This is better than 'everything is the same as Kew Gardens', but suffers from the problem that only five studies existed that could provide suitable hedgehog densities. All of those had taken place in the summer, at which time the hedgehogs were breeding, and so the populations contained young hedgehogs and were at far higher densities than they would have been at the end of winter, before breeding started. The authors had to make what amounted to educated guesses about hedgehog breeding rates in various habitats, and adjust the densities accordingly. The estimate they came up with was one and a half million hedgehogs, but they were upfront about its limitations. It could have been off the mark by an unknowable amount – for example, if any of the five studies they cited had by chance examined a hedgehog population that was atypical of a given type of habitat, or made in an atypically good or bad year.

In 2017 another group of researchers tried a variant of the same approach, using a statistical model to match published hedgehog density estimates with the geographical locations where the studies had taken place, and to see what other places had similar habitat characteristics. And the national population estimate came out as somewhere between three-quarters of a million and twelve million hedgehogs (i.e.

relatively few or quite a lot, really; who knows?). And again, in 2018, yet another attempt yielded 552,000 hedgehogs, but with the authors scoring the figure's reliability as just two out of five.

Fun question: based only on the *reliable* available evidence, what really happened to our hedgehogs between 1950 and 2018? Answer: no idea. And did we really lose two-thirds of hedgehogs between 1995 and 2018 – or even 39 per cent, adjusting for the differences in habitat definitions suggested by the 2018 report? Maybe; but then what about the possible 12 million (or 10, 9, 8, 7, 6 million etc.) in 2017? The estimates – and this is nobody's fault – are so imprecise as to be unusable.

National estimates of mammal numbers make for appealing headline stats. But they are *awful* as indicators of what's actually happening. If they were based on tonnes of individual annual surveys, we could trust the figures. But they weren't, so we can't. And worse, the old surveys quickly become obsolete. If the hedgehog population is changing, then even the studies cited in the 1995 report – now twenty-seven years ago – may well be nothing but snapshots of an entirely different reality.

The wider problem is that hedgehogs are, to use the technical term, a right swine to survey.* While nationally widespread, they can be thin on the ground and very mobile.† They make little effort to stay hidden, true, but their propensity to roam causes serious headaches.‡ You can head out at night with a torch and do a census, or capture them, mark them (for example with bright bits of heat-shrink tubing to create a multicoloured spiny spectacular) and let them go again over several nights to estimate the minimum numbers around. But to convert the raw count into a density – required for a national estimate – you must first know how large an area the

---

* Yes indeed, pun fully intended.

† In contrast to hedgehogs that have been run over, which are thin on the ground and quite immobile.

‡ There's a rather wonderful anecdote from Lauren Moore, whom we'll meet properly before the end of the chapter. She lost a male hedgehog she was radio-tracking for her studies. He completely vanished. With a lot of effort, her team searched the local area, and eventually found that he had upped sticks and hiked many kilometres away before deciding to cross the M6 motorway on a footbridge (i.e. he headed up the ramp, trotted over all the cars and lorries, and clambered back down the other side). He hung around in a field there for a bit before crossing back over and never visiting that field again. They can move about *a lot*.

hedgehogs are using. And that is not straightforward. Spotting five hedgehogs in a 10 × 10m garden, for example, does not imply that there are five per 100m² in the general locality. Those hedgehogs might visit a large number of gardens over the course of a night, and could be nesting somewhere else entirely. Estimating their density would mean intensively searching all of the possible habitats they might be using until you could be sure you hadn't missed any possible locations, or indeed any other hedgehogs. One way to achieve this would be to radio-track, which requires you to capture animals and attach radio transmitters so you can find them again using, essentially, a fantastically unwieldy TV aerial.* You would

---

* With most animals the transmitter is on a collar. But this doesn't work on animals with a thick neck and a thin head, even if said neck weren't protected by a forest of pointy things and the whole beast wasn't then able to roll into a ball, making any attached collar a potentially severe inconvenience. The only way to get a radio tag on a hedgehog is to trim a patch of spines (like cutting fingernails) and glue the tag in place (avoiding all contact with skin). This is time-consuming and the result looks so unattractive that researchers often get abuse from people worried about what's being done to their hedgehogs. The concern is understandable, but – as one researcher told me – when you're losing sleep, and people are saying horrible things because they don't understand, it makes you feel kind of

need to do that night after night until you have enough locations to be sure about their range size. And that's a lot of work.

Other techniques for assessing hedgehog populations
involve setting out plastic tunnels that capture hedgehogs'
footprints,* if and when they deign to pass through. This
is less effort than surveying on the hoof, but you need a good
few tunnels, each spaced more than 100m from the next, to
have a fair chance of capturing a hedgehog print. And they
need to be left *in situ* for at least four days, and then gathered
in and the paper analysed. The latter is made trickier by the
plethora of mucky-footed wildlife that will have wandered in
and out, chewed up the paper, had a scratch, done a poo etc.
But it is a nice, reliable way of assessing whether hedgehogs
are present or not. It remains labour-intensive, though, and

---

unappreciated. The tags also fall off once the spines start to regrow, so
you have a limited time window in which to get data from your
hedgehog. Nightmare.

* There's an ink-pad at each end, and what begins life as a sheet of
white paper in the middle. You can also add some food to encourage
the hedgehogs in. If you're lucky you'll return to find a lovely set of
perfect spindly footprints trekking gaily across the paper. If you're
unlucky you'll return to a torn-up, brown-smeared, pulpy mess of
unidentifiable damp weirdness.

also suffers from not being able to give you direct counts of how many individuals you have.

It takes time, money and skilled researchers to derive accurate numbers and densities for hedgehogs. Far too few projects over the years have had enough of any of these. So we must rely on other sources of data to reveal what has befallen our hedgehogs – preferably data that cover a good few decades so we can see a proper trend.

Somewhat ironically, the longest-running dataset we have comes not from people trying to conserve hedgehogs, but from folks trying to get rid of them. Gamekeepers have controlled hedgehog populations for hundreds of years, largely because hedgehogs are partial to snacking on the eggs of ground-nesting birds. As a macabre aside – one to thicken and spice our murderous mystery soup – although we tend not to think of Mrs Tiggy-Winkle as being particularly blood-thirsty, behind her twinkly eyes and impeccably starched aprons lurk some rather dark deeds.* Richard Yarnell of Nottingham Trent University and his team have spent a lot of time studying hedgehogs up on North Ronaldsay in the

---

* There's at least one body buried beneath her nice clean flagstone floor, and she'll thank you not to go prying, if you please'm.

Orkney archipelago, and estimate that hedgehogs there account for about a third of all the predation of ground-nesting bird eggs. This puts the impact of hedgehog egg-snaffling on a par with the combined efforts of crows and gulls.* And it's not only eggs. Richard told me a story handed on from the researchers at Ronaldsay's bird observatory who in 2021 came across a hedgehog tucking into an almost fully fledged fulmar chick. The chick protested while the hedgehog, for at least some of the proceedings, was merrily eating it alive. Similarly, researchers on the Uists have found bits of curlew chick legs that look decidedly hog-munched.

Good Mrs Tiggy-Winkle therefore hasn't always endeared herself to folks who nurture ground-nesting birds. And when those birds have provided people's livelihoods, the backlash has

---

* The hedgehogs have a great technique for getting at the nests: they charge. If they find, say, a black-headed gull sitting on its eggs, they simply run at it and knock it off. If you've ever seen hedgehogs pushing each other around it's a similar kind of manoeuvre. Except the birds can't really fight back. They can try a little bit and peck at the hedgehog a couple of times, but they quickly realize that they're just not going to make an impression on those spines. Then they leave the hedgehog free to start chomping their eggs.

been furious. In *The Hedgehog*, Maurice Burton cites church-
wardens' accounts from the late seventeenth century in which
rewards were offered of 'a penny each for 1002 urchins', as
well as twopence a head in Westmoreland and, in the nine-
teenth century, fourpence a head in Oxfordshire and
Bedfordshire. Such anecdotes suggest that thousands of
hedgehogs per parish were meeting untimely demises thanks
to their (admittedly deserved) reputation for eating eggs and
(unproven but perhaps plausible) reputation for drinking
milk from cows' udders. And during the nineteenth-century
boom in pheasant shooting, keepers reputedly set up gibbets
containing 150–200 hedgehog carcasses, and boasted of killing thirty a night with dogs. How seriously we should take
these numbers is debatable, but they do indicate a hedgehog
population abundant enough to be perceived as a nuisance –
and that the snuffly little criminals have withstood hefty
persecution over several centuries.

Systematic data on hedgehog culling efforts began to be collected in 1961, as part of the National Gamebag Census of
around 650 British shooting estates. The data are still being
collected today and are expressed as numbers of animals killed
per unit area, to provide a measure called 'bag density'. A
report from 2009 shows that between 1961 and 2007 the bag

density of hedgehogs effectively halved – numbers killed per unit area decreased by 48 per cent.*

Even if not as drastic as the 98 per cent decline originally suggested, hedgehog numbers halving in forty years is cause for alarm. But there are problems with relying on these figures, too. In 1981 hedgehogs received partial protection under the Wildlife and Countryside Act, which made it unlawful to kill them deliberately, or to set a trap with the intention of catching them. In response, many gamekeepers stopped culling them. And those that didn't might have thought twice before reporting that to anyone.† The upshot of the change in legislation is that hedgehogs can now only be legitimately

---

* The report is perhaps understandably coy about stating raw numbers of animals killed, to the extent where the data are simply not provided for any of the species being shot. What we get instead is a percentage increase or decrease relative to the first year.

† A minority of gamekeepers view adherence to wildlife laws as optional. I remember going out round an estate with one who told me that he applied for grants for creating otter holts, then stuck fen traps (lethal, metal snap traps) around each of them, to make sure that the otter cubs wouldn't get any big ideas concerning the estate's fish. I kept my mouth shut at the time because I suspected he was trying to wind me up, because I was in his Land Rover and because he had a gun. Contemporary reports of ospreys and hen harriers being poisoned do

killed or captured by accident, in traps set for other species (e.g. rats, grey squirrels, stoats and weasels). Game-bag records from 1981 onwards, therefore, should only really contain hedgehogs as by-catch. And, frustratingly, this means that the post-1981 data are not at all comparable with the pre-1981 data.

An updated analysis using only data from 1981 and 2019 shows that the number of sites reporting at least one trapped hedgehog fell from 174 in the former year to twenty-one in the latter. That's a drop of 88 per cent in thirty-nine years. And the updated bag index reveals that hedgehogs recorded per unit area (i.e. the number of hedgehogs blundering into traps set for other species) declined by half over that period. But again, there are problems with the data. The numbers reported reflect numbers of hedgehogs, yes, but also the amount of effort going into setting traps, as well as how willing game-keepers are to admit that they've killed a protected species. So although the game-bag data are suggestive of a decline, unless rates of trapping and reporting remained unchanged (which we don't know, because there is no information on either), the

---

rather suggest that negative attitudes towards wildlife remain hard to shift in some quarters.

data could well show a decline even if hedgehog numbers were stable. Not massively reliable, unfortunately.

What else have we got? Well, the next longest-running con-tinuous survey data on hedgehogs comes from the British Trust for Ornithology's Breeding Birds Survey – which asks volunteers to survey randomly allocated sites in Britain for bird species and which since 1995 has asked them to include hedgehog sightings. The results show a 66 per cent decline in hedgehogs between 1995 and 2007, and a slightly later analy-sis shows a 77 per cent decline in hedgehogs between 2002 and 2019. But, rather crucially, the BTO survey was not designed primarily to record hedgehogs. It takes place during the day, when hedgehogs aren't active. Records therefore often represent broad presence or absence based on field signs and local knowledge. So although it's another independent survey showing a decline, it stops well short of putting the whole issue beyond doubt. The data could be influenced by external factors, like changes in the expertise and local knowledge of the surveyors.

Yet another approach to examining hedgehog population trends involved researchers comparing data from a contem-poraneous citizen science project (HogWatch, run since 2000 by the People's Trust for Endangered Species and the

British Hedgehog Preservation Society) with previous citizen science records of hedgehog sightings collected between 1960 and 1975. For each dataset the researchers divided England into grid cells and calculated how many had at least one sighting of hedgehogs. Between 1960 and 1975, hedgehogs were spotted in nearly three-quarters of the grid cells. Between 2000 and 2015, adjusting for a much larger number of surveyors, hedgehogs were seen in the equivalent of two-thirds of cells. This suggested a decrease in hedgehog occupancy of England of about 5–7 per cent.

Seven per cent doesn't sound particularly alarming, does it? Had all the other methods vastly overestimated the hedgehog's plight? Maybe. But the 7 per cent figure might be a substantial underestimate. Recording only presence or absence is rather coarse. A single record of a lone hedgehog in one garden would be enough to make a given grid cell 'positive' for the species. If somebody set England ablaze, sparing only people's gardens, that could decimate hedgehog numbers but not really change their measured occupancy much. So things could conceivably be far, far worse than the 5–7 per cent the study was able to suggest.

All these independent data sources reveal declines in hedgehog numbers – but declines of vastly different scope and scale.

And all the sources contain potentially fatal unknowns and biases. We probably can't fully trust any of them.

Frustrating, isn't it?

The Detective's gaze settles on Mr Clarkson's truculent form. He, in turn, turns a baleful eye to the room.

'What a load of old tosh,' he declares. He stands up. 'Hedgehogs don't mix with cars and that isn't my fault. They should stick to hedges.' He strides to the window, throws open the curtain and gesticulates at the crime scene. 'I see stuff like this the whole time. Every year hedgehogs are flattened in their thousands. And that means they can't be scarce, doesn't it? And look, is anyone out there even a qualified vet? I mean, how can you be sure the damned hedgehog is even dead?'

The Detective flips through her notebook. Damn. None of the evidence seems to have withstood scrutiny, and some is downright contradictory. And Mr Clarkson's folded arms and smirk say that he knows as much. She is sure she has the right information to wipe that look from his face, though. Somewhere. But as the pages flick by she has to admit that pinning anything on this suspect is proving more troublesome than she would like. At this rate she'll have to go out herself and start examining the hedgehog's corpse. If indeed it actually is a corpse . . .

*

34

The Detective is not alone. Many hedgehog researchers have struggled to establish beyond doubt that hedgehogs are declining nationally. The problem is that all of the data, of course, require some sort of counting of hedgehogs. And, as I have mentioned, that is hard to do at scale because they move about a lot. If only there were some way to get the hedgehogs to stay still long enough to be counted, then to mobilize a large number of volunteers – none of whom would need a lot of expertise or to go far out of their way to contribute – to go out and find them. Wouldn't that be nice?

Two words: roadkill surveys.

Oh yes. Just watch Mr Clarkson's smile turn sickly. One of the best sources of information on hedgehog population trends comes in the form of the sad little flat, spiny discs that we see embedded in the tarmac of our roads. Dead hedgehogs definitely stay put long enough to be counted. Why head out at night with a torch when passing traffic can, in effect, sample the hedgehog population for you?*

---

* Shamefully, some early ecologists actively applied similar sampling regimes, sometimes heading out with the intention of killing every individual animal in the area they wanted to survey. It can yield a very accurate population estimate. But of course once they were done there wasn't a lot of population left. Thankfully the approach, for terrestrial

The idea was first put into action way back in the 1950s by a single researcher counting the number of squashed hedgehogs he encountered on his car journeys over a two-year period. He converted these into a simple, standard measure of hedgehogs per 100 miles. His approach, though, was ad hoc and the numbers not terribly reliable. The technique was substantially improved and weaponized by the living legend that is Pat Morris in the 1990s, using an army of volunteers who were given a standard protocol to follow. The data, collected over five years from 1990 to 1994, enlisted hundreds of observers who between them travelled 162,043 miles and counted 5,321 dead hedgehogs. As well as providing a brilliant baseline for future surveys, a key finding of the study was that the quantities of incurably prostrate insectivores* varied markedly between different regions of Britain. In the north-east there were 6.66 hedgehogs per 100 miles, for example,

---

vertebrates at least, fell out of favour many decades ago. The technique is somewhat euphemistically called *destructive sampling*. Because 'We destructively sampled the population' sounds a lot more professional than 'We stomped on, gassed, shot or otherwise terminally inconvenienced some hapless wildlife so we could do a study.'

* I have been trying hard not to use the words 'flat' and 'squashed' too often. This may have resulted in some linguistic contortions.

whereas in the south-west this number was 1.23. These variations were probably not down to differences in roads (which should be relatively consistent across regions), but likely to represent real-world population differences. They also hinted that some factor other than traffic could be affecting hedgehogs differently in different parts of the UK.

In 2001 the People's Trust for Endangered Species took up the road-survey mantle. They launched the Mammals on Roads (MoR) initiative, asking the public to report sightings of both carcasses and live mammals on their car journeys. In the first year, data from 2,081 journeys recorded 10,689 mammals (not all dead, but still that's a heck of a lot of ex-wildlife), of which 2,607 were hedgehogs. And the survey has been running ever since.

The trend the MoR data reveal looks bad.* The first four years (2001–4) recorded an average of 1.45 hedgehogs per 100km. By comparison, Pat Morris's survey ten years earlier had recorded an average of 2.05 hedgehogs per 100km. Between these two surveys, which used almost identical

---

* If you think this sentence reads a bit weirdly it's probably because I use 'data' in the plural (because it's one datum, many data), and most people don't. Data are plural. And I'm a pedant.

methodology, the number of hedgehogs being hit by cars fell by a third. And things did not improve from there. By 2014 the number of hedgehog casualties had fallen again, this time to 0.62 per 100km, a number that stayed roughly similar until 2018 (the last year for which data had been analysed at the time of writing). Just looking at these very crude estimates gives an impression of a hedgehog population on a steep downward trajectory – in twenty-eight years the number being killed by vehicles has decreased by 70 per cent.

We really would want to see a lot more hedgehogs than that being run over. Yes, please read that again. I can't quite believe I wrote it. But higher numbers of road casualties would indicate the existence of more hedgehogs at large in the wider landscape, and that hedgehog populations are doing well.* Instead, the MoR data pull us firmly back towards believing in a drastic hedgehog decline. But there's yet another bump in the road, if you'll forgive the expression. To infer a population decline from roadkill requires

---

* A tip of the hat here to the wonderful David Wembridge – who has been analysing these road data for years and whose findings have done amazing things for hedgehog conservation – for this rather dissonant observation.

that more hedgehogs at large in the landscape means more hedgehogs crossing roads, in turn translating into more road collisions and higher counts of the resultant prostrate wafers. And we must ask if those assumptions are justified. Because if they're not, the survey wouldn't be a good measure of actual hedgehog numbers.

As a thought experiment, imagine a country road with a few cars a day, surrounded by hedgerows full of hedgehogs. Despite a lot of road crossings, the hedgehogs would have to be pretty unlucky to get hit. Few corpses. Now, imagine that the road gets widened, and traffic is directed down it at higher speeds, to the tune of hundreds of cars per hour. The number of collisions goes right up. Many corpses. This clearly does not indicate an increase in the local abundance of hedgehogs, not least because a new source of mortality has just been introduced. Hedgehog roadkill is a measure not just of their abundance, but of traffic volume, which has been increasing steadily ever since records began. It's tempting to conclude that, 'Oh, well, that's okay, because we would expect hedgehog collisions to increase with traffic volume, and actually they're going down – meaning the lower numbers probably do represent a real-world decline.' Unfortunately, we can't conclude this without testing whether the presence of, *too many* cars might start to deter hedgehogs from crossing roads (resulting in the appearance of a decline).

The relationship between numbers of cars and numbers of hedgehog collisions is tricksy. Do noise, vibrations and smell prevent hedgehogs from stepping on to tarmac? They might. Studies, albeit from only eight radio-tracked hedgehogs, have suggested that hedgehogs tend to avoid crossing roads, especially wider ones, and that motorways might represent barriers to hedgehog movements.* Such barriers potentially fragment hedgehog populations into smaller, more vulnerable units. Also, what if only a proportion of any given hedgehog population was bold enough to venture across the road in the first place? Those hedgehogs would be far more likely to sally forth, have a nasty accident, and be counted. And over time the surviving hedgehogs would end up disproportionately representing timid non-road-crossers. So there are a few ways that busy roads might reduce the number of hedgehogs prepared to cross them. And therefore that hedgehogs could be perfectly present, but wisely not risking their lives for the sake of a survey.

---

* Unless, of course, the road is the M6, there's a handy footbridge near by and the hedgehog is determined to perplex a researcher.

Thankfully there is some evidence to help us unpick all this. A suite of rather grim studies of various wildlife – including racoons, rabbits and white-tailed deer – have shown a good correlation between road casualties and numbers in the wider landscape. One of my own students in 2018 found that numbers of foxes and badgers being recorded in the MoR survey had often increased in places where hedgehog numbers decreased. These observations suggest that there's nothing inherent in traffic that puts wildlife off crossing roads. But of course, the fact that other animals are prone to ending up as part of the scenery doesn't mean the same is necessarily true of hedgehogs. We do know, however, that hedgehogs and rabbits respond in a similar way to different road types: the wider the road, the more of both species get hit by cars. The study that demonstrated this couldn't separate out the effects of how busy the roads were, because road width and traffic volume are clearly correlated (busy roads tend to be wider), but did come to a telling conclusion about how hedgehogs are likely to perceive roads. It said that 'for both rabbits and hedgehogs the vast majority of the rural road network is likely to be perceived as free from risk of oncoming vehicles' but also that 'because traffic speeds are high compared with speeds of mammal road crossing, even risk-averse road-crossing mammals are at risk from collisions with vehicles'.

To put it another way, most rural roads won't have enough traffic to put hedgehogs off – especially at night, when hedgehogs are active – but if a car does happen along they won't be fast enough to scuttle out of the way. (But rabbits probably will be – they were about thirty-two times less likely to be killed than hedgehogs.) This finding is backed up by another study showing that for a range of species, from barn owls to foxes, hedgehogs and rabbits, increasing the traffic volume on major, multi-lane highways simply led to more of each species being hit. And an early test of roadkill-counts in 2005 found that 68 per cent of squashed hedgehogs were sighted on A-roads; 18 per cent on B-roads; and 13 per cent on 'minor' roads. These data don't suggest too much avoidance with increasing traffic. Which is good news for our confidence in road-survey data.

And with that confidence we can *finally* arrive at a firm conclusion. There are few convincing alternative explanations for our current lack of hedgehog road casualties. Numbers of hedgehogs killed on our roads have fallen by 70 per cent in three decades, and the most plausible and simplest explanation is that there are now fewer hedgehogs surrounding those roads. Taken together with the (albeit potentially flawed) data supplied by gamekeepers (showing a 48 per cent decline in hedgehogs in game bags between 1981 and 2019) and bird enthusiasts (showing that evidence of hedgehog presence fell by 77 per cent between 2002 and 2009), the road data make a compelling case. In rural areas, in which all these surveys took place, we actually do seem to be in the midst of a crisis of disappearing hedgehogs.

'All right, all right,' says Mr Clarkson, 'let's say I agree there's a serial killer on the loose. Fine. But it could be any of us. What makes you think that I'm to blame?'

His question turns heads among the other guests.

'You mean aside from the corpses covered in tyre-tracks?' says the Detective.

'That's not murder, that's accidents,' says Mr Clarkson. 'Thousands of humans get killed in traffic every year, too. And it's not like the number of people is going down. So how do we know something else entirely isn't doing for all these hedgehogs?'

And that is rather the issue. We have established a decline, but we are no closer to understanding whether traffic is causing it. The number of hedgehogs being killed by cars annually is huge, certainly. In the ten years between 2001 and 2011 the

MoR database recorded 11,979 hedgehogs, of which 99 per cent were dead. But human road casualties over the last four years (2018–21) have also sadly totalled 6,384 people, which as a ballpark figure is roughly equivalent to the hedgehog numbers per annum. I'm not seeking to draw an equivalence between the severity of hedgehog and human traffic deaths, but vehicles are very unfortunately a source of mortality for both species, though not one that necessarily affects our conservation status. That said, we (I hope) know the total numbers of humans killed down to the last individual, whereas national hedgehog road deaths are going to be a lot more than those recorded by citizen scientists.

Earlier in this chapter I gave our best estimates for how many hedgehogs are being killed on the roads in one year as likely to fall between 167,000 and 335,000. That's a lot, but we cannot put those figures into context, by calculating what proportion of all living British hedgehogs they represent, because that requires taking a somewhat imprecise estimate of annual total roadkill and dividing it by a wholly inaccurate estimate of the total live hedgehog population to derive something almost completely useless.

To get a handle on how bad road deaths are for hedgehog populations, we need to change the scale at which we examine the issue. Detailed work on local populations should reveal how much they are individually affected. One attempt in the Netherlands studied hedgehogs in pairs of habitats. In fifteen study locations the researchers set up one plot well away from roads, and another right next to a road. They used footprint tunnels to assess how many hedgehogs were present in each. They found that numbers next to the roads were approximately 30 per cent lower than the numbers further away from roads. But this being hedgehogs, the difference was *just* shy of being statistically valid, because their experiment as set up could only reliably detect differences of 35 per cent or greater. Also, some of the 'further away' plots were within 800m of a road and so the hedgehog populations there might still have suffered from some road mortality. Overall, there probably was a difference, and it probably was caused by the roads, but irritatingly this study is another addition to the pantheon of research projects unable to put the whole 'car issue' beyond doubt.

More work on hedgehog populations on the local scale is happening. Lauren Moore is a PhD student studying hedgehogs around the UK, and the primary objective of her research is to find out what proportion of a given local hedgehog population is killed by traffic every year. This is the focus of four of her study populations in Nottingham-shire, and the preliminary results are intriguing. So far, somewhere between 10 per cent and 31 per cent of the hedgehogs there are being killed on the roads every year. That's not ideal, but the numbers might just be low enough to make road deaths insufficient to cause a decline by them-selves. The hedgehogs might be able to compensate by breeding. Especially because the hedgehogs getting killed are mainly males.

Male hedgehog road collisions peak in June and July, which is when they are recklessly heading out in obedience to a com-pulsion to find mates.* Females do get killed, and have their own peak of deaths in September (trying to lay down fat reserves for the winter), but overall Lauren found that males comprised around 69 per cent of the hedgehogs killed on the roads. Similar results have been found not just in Britain but in separate studies in Sweden (80 per cent males) and Ireland (64 per cent males). And the thing about losing males is that from a population perspective it isn't necessarily a big prob-lem. If a female dies, that's all of her potential babies gone. If a male dies, another one will soon step up and take his place,

---

* A lesson here for any teenagers reading.

probably looking happily perplexed at his good fortune. So unless male numbers are reduced to a very low level,* breeding rates will be primarily determined by the number of reproductive females. And they tend not to be the ones killed by traffic.

This, finally, could be Mr Clarkson's saving grace. The sheer numbers of road casualties will of course have a substantial effect on hedgehog numbers; but it's an effect that, to some extent at least, it seems they could compensate for. From that perspective the right hedgehogs are dying on our roads. And so we simply cannot, from the evidence, conclude that traffic is *the* key factor sending hedgehog numbers spiralling downwards. It could be something else entirely. And that 'something' must be investigated.

'It seems that there's an inconvenient truth around here,' says Mr Clarkson. 'It's that you've got nothing on me. I'm a driver, not a murderer.' He glares around him. 'And while you've all been pointing fingers you missed the crucial bit. I've been paying attention to what was said.' He turns to face a dark figure at the

---

* Such that the remaining males are too knackered to cope with the demands on them.

back of the room. 'And what I heard is that it's not only cars and hedgehogs that don't mix. What I heard is that we get fewer hedgehogs where we get more of one other animal in particular. And that just seems a bit coincidental to me.' He grins. 'Isn't that right, Tommy Brock?'

CHAPTER 3

The Tale of Tommy Brock

The badgers are moving the goalposts.

OWEN PATERSON,
former Environment Secretary

SPRING 2020 IN KIRTLINGTON, OXFORDSHIRE, IS unseasonably dry. And the warm night air is alive with screaming. The cries are despairing, raw and frightened. The sort that stop you dead. They aren't human, but it takes you long moments to be sure. The sound carries all the indignant vulnerability of a newborn's howl, but with a cat-like, animalistic quality that brings your head up, and makes your breath come faster. You could persuade yourself that it's okay, that it's just a fox calling. But you wouldn't be convinced. Something in the sound is not quite right. And there may well be a darker explanation – that it's an animal in mortal terror. This could be the screaming of a hedgehog being eaten alive by a badger.*

---

* There is a video hosted on a well-known platform entitled 'Hedgehog screaming in fear after being attacked by a badger' and it's a tough watch. I wouldn't recommend it unless you are morbidly curious or writing a book on the subject or something.

I have visited Kirtlington, and it's beautiful. The village is all thick old stone walls, quaint churchiness and quintessential Englishness. The atmosphere is warm and welcoming. And this is especially the case if you're a hedgehog. Because the village takes its hedgehogs very seriously indeed.* Thanks to the magnificent efforts of the Kirtlington Wildlife and Conservation Society, those thick old stone walls are shot through with modern hedgehog holes. Height differences between gardens have been solved with ingenuity – here a beautifully crafted wooden ramp, there stone steps or staircases, up and down all of which hedgehogs speed-waddle on their nightly rounds. We know these innovations are doing their job because of infra-red footage from the cameras that monitor them. And other households have camera traps set to watch over the hedgehog feeding stations they have created. All of this makes Kirtlington a hedgehog paradise. And all of this is why the village was so perfectly placed to record the disappearance of its hedgehogs.

---

* So much so that they have made the national news on more than one occasion and – I kid you not – have been endorsed by none other than Dolly Parton, who turns out to be a hedgehog fan. No sarcasm intended, or indeed possible, when I say that latter endorsement can only mean that you're doing something truly spectacular in the world.

Day one, 5 May 2020, and a householder reports that no hedgehogs have visited for a couple of weeks. The next day another says that they'd found a badger in the garden, and also the carcass of a dead hedgehog. The carcass, they said, consisted only of 'skin and prickles'. Nine days later and another house records its first ever night with no hedgehog visits. And yet another says that of the four hedgehogs it expects, only two are now visiting. Over the next four days these two are reduced to one. And two weeks later to zero. And things stay that way. An appeal to the wider community yields more responses: six further reports of hedgehogs and/or of their droppings vanishing from gardens; four reports of badgers being seen in the village; three reports of badgers in the village's surroundings, including one youngster found dead and emaciated in Kirtlington Park. And finally, of course, there were those raw, despairing screams.

The good news is that the village's hedgehogs did not entirely vanish. The bad news is that they came very, very close. And it's clear that Tommy Brock and his mates are prime suspects. What is less clear is what could have driven the badgers into the village in the first place, and the extent to which they were directly responsible for the hedgehogs' disappearance. Badgers usually don't like to be around humans and their structures. In a recent camera study of hedgehogs and badgers in rural locations, 70 per cent of the badgers snapped were 200m or more away from buildings, and only 5 per cent of the cameras in amenity grasslands (i.e. parks and football pitches near villages) spotted a badger. So we need to know what prompted the badgers to enter the village. And also in need of explanation is what might have happened to those disappeared hedgehogs. At least one ended up as badger nourishment, that much is certain. Badgers can and do eat hedgehogs;*† and the 'just skin and prickles' carcass bespeaks

---

* To quote from the *The Sword in the Stone* by T. H. White: ' "Hedge-pig," said the Wart, peering at this victim with blurred, short-sighted eyes, "I am going to munch you up." The hedgehog . . . woke up at this and squealed most lamentably. "The more you squeal," said the Wart, "the more I shall gnash. It makes my blood boil within me." ' There you have it. It's one of my favourite books, and I will defend to the death (although possibly not *my* death) the position that there is no finer source of natural-historical storytelling available to the discerning child reader.

† And it's not only in the UK, by the way. One of my colleagues has been radio-tracking hedgehogs in Denmark, and the same happens there. She followed one particular hog right to the edge of a forest edge and then heard shooting. The Danish hunting season had begun, which made creeping around the forest in the early hours a

an unfurling by an animal with powerful claws, the thus-exposed soft bits forming a rather ghastly packed lunch. But what happened to the remainder?

To begin with the badger incursion, the most probable explanation is the climate. Yes, really. The clues are scattered through the story. You see, it was a warm night, and bone dry. Indeed, spring 2020 was one of the driest – and the sunniest – on record. And as a result, the young, emaciated badger found dead in Kirtlington Park had probably died of starvation. Because if you're a badger a dry spring is not a good thing. The survival of both juveniles and adults is massively affected by a lack of rain, especially early in the year.* This is because

---

near-suicidally stupid thing to do. And so she was left with a typical field ecologist's dilemma: lose data or risk death. She opted to continue tracking. (That right there tells you everything you need to know about conservation researchers.) A few days later she found the hedgehog dead. It had met a hungry badger, to its terminal detriment. The loss of a study animal can be horrible, but in this instance it swung the death/data decision firmly in favour of not getting shot at . . . so she was quite relieved.

* Extreme weather in general is bad for wildlife. Too much rain in spring, for example, might be fine for adult badgers, but again can have a bad effect on juveniles, this time probably because time spent cold and wet exposes a youngster to the risk of hypothermia, and also

badgers need to eat earthworms by the bucketful just to stay up on their paws. And hot, dry conditions make digging up enough of the things a tough job. So the badgers came to the village most probably because they were half starved. The village might be scary, but its gardens were filled with food and water left out for hedgehogs. Both the food and the hedgehogs themselves would make a more-than-acceptable-thank-you addition to a hungry badger's diet. So the temptations are plain. And who knows, maybe the fact that Britain was in pandemic lockdown, and we humans were keeping indoors much more than usual, also tipped the badgers in favour of risking it. In any event it looks like the badgers entered, stage right, and the hedgehogs vanished. What is unknown is whether they vanished down the badgers, whether they scarpered to avoid that fate, or whether the hot weather put the hedgehogs themselves under food and water stress, forcing them to try their luck elsewhere. My personal suspicion rests heavily on the badgers.

---

makes it more susceptible to a particularly nasty parasitic infection. If folks tell you that climate change won't have an impact on the whole of the natural world, they are very wrong.

A question studied by hog-watchers is whether hedgehogs are scared of badgers, how you can tell, and what the consequences would be. It's not just an academic exercise. The answer has implications for what would befall hedgehogs if badger numbers rose and they found themselves sharing their habitat with lots of unpleasantly voracious housemates. There is a whole field of ecology dedicated to what is known as 'the landscape of fear' and how it affects prey animals. Predators influence prey in two different ways. Obviously they can kill them and eat them, which does rather tend to curtail a given prey animal's future activities – so the predation has direct ecological impacts. But predators also scare their prey, causing them to divert time into being hyper-vigilant. This simple behavioural shift can have some unexpectedly profound real-world implications. As an example, when grizzly bears are around, moose have been shown to keep their heads up for longer, and stay on the move to avoid being eaten. This in turn reduces the impacts of moose-browsing on willow trees, which flourish. And in flourishing they become a haven for songbirds. You wouldn't normally suspect that songbirds could benefit from what bears get up to, but they do – because of the complex ways in which seemingly slight changes can cascade down food chains. Similarly, the landscape of fear is credited with stopping herbivore populations in Yellowstone National Park getting too uppity now wolves are back. Without wolves, previous generations happily put their heads down and blitzed the plants with impunity. But with wolves around, the herbivores now balance time spent browsing against time spent avoiding getting browsed. In short, the wolves worry the elk, the elk spend more time with their heads up, and moving around, and this gives the trees and shrubs space to regenerate. Wolves, bears – and fear in general – turn out to be quite a good thing, ecologically. Although the elk probably disagree.

Badgers are not quite to hedgehogs what wolves are to elk.* But they certainly give them the heebie-jeebies. This was shown very neatly in a study of four sites, all a mixture of villages and farmland. At two of these, hedgehogs had the place to themselves, and the other two they shared with badgers.

---

* You don't get packs of badgers harrying fleeing hedgehogs and circling around to pick off the weak. More usually they'll bumble into one other and the badger might have a go if it's hungry, or in a mood or something.

Well, I say 'shared'. It didn't work out that way. At the non-badgered sites, about 40 per cent of the hedgehogs' activity was in the village, the rest in the surrounding fields. By comparison, at one badger site the hedgehogs steadfastly refused to leave the village. And in general, across both badger sites 65 per cent of the hedgehogs' time was spent near buildings. Looking at how the hedgehogs used the fields (excluding the site where they didn't), the researchers found that without badgers the hedgehogs were ranging about 42m away from hedges and field edges, but where there were badgers this dropped to 4m. Clinging to cover is not the behaviour of an animal happily confident in its ability to survive. And of course that change in behaviour may well have some serious consequences for the hedgehogs' ability to feed themselves. Restricting their activities to narrow bands of habitat alongside hedges might risk limiting their access to the invertebrate food on which they depend. With badgers around, the hedgehogs were excluded from the fields and confined to edges and villages. And there's one more twist here: at the sites with badgers, total invertebrate availability (aka the amount of scuttley-type hedgehog food) was lower than at the sites without them. We don't know whether the badgers were responsible for the lower numbers of invertebrates in that study. But a real bummer for hedgehogs is that badgers like to eat a lot of the same things that they do.*

Hedgehogs eat a wide variety of invertebrates. Badgers also eat a wide variety of invertebrates. Both species appear partial to worms, but this is especially true of badgers, for which they make up 50–90 per cent of their diet. There is a bit of scope from various diet studies for claiming that hedgehogs and badgers aren't going after exactly the same invertebrates, and so might be able to avoid directly competing for the same food. But still the situation is pretty weird. A hedgehog, an insectivore with an adult weight of somewhere between 400 grams and 1.2 kilos, is beautifully designed to go after beetles, caterpillars, earthworms, earwigs, slugs, snails and all things crunchy, slimy or downright creepy. Badgers, on the other hand, have an average adult weight of 11–12 kilos, and are built like tanks. They have powerful jaws and impressive mobility. What they are doing eating invertebrates is anyone's guess. Almost every other self-respecting carnivore that big heads out and hunts down decent-sized prey. But for our Eurasian badger there's tonnes of food crawling about, so why

---

* There do seem to be quite a lot of real bummers associated with being a hedgehog in modern Britain, don't there?

chase the fast stuff? In fact the only other prey most badgers will take are the occasional unwary rodent – and, of course, hedgehogs (which can't outrun them and for which curling up offers little protection – so oh dear, basically).

At this point you'd be entitled to wonder quite what the badgers' problem is. Even when the dratted things aren't directly consuming hedgehogs they're terrifying them so much they can't eat, and *then* scoffing down their only source of food. It's ecological bullying, pure and simple.* And so it comes as little surprise that a large variety of research has shown that hedgehogs tend to be found where badgers aren't. We've already encountered this phenomenon – in the previous chapter, where areas with a lot of roadkill badgers and foxes were shown to have fewer roadkill hedgehogs. And there's plenty more evidence. Numbers of hedgehogs in both rural and suburban habitats in Oxfordshire have been shown to rise with increasing distance from the nearest badgers. The abundance of hedgehogs and badgers appears to be inversely

---

* Well, actually it's asymmetrical intraguild predation, which is ecologist-speak for 'Oh, so both species are eating the same stuff, but one of them is massive and eats the other one too. Print me some datasheets, this is about to get interesting!'

correlated on farmland, so farms with fewer badgers and major roads, and more hedgerows, are far more likely to have hedgehogs. And two citizen science surveys that examined the presence of hedgehogs and badgers nationally found essentially that hedgehogs tended to be wherever badgers weren't.* Badgers were particularly common in the south and west of England. And guess where the hedgehogs were? Not there, basically – to the extent that the study's authors suspected that hedgehogs are now preferentially found in habitats that they don't like very much (basically arable fields), simply because in rural Britain everywhere else is badger-infested.

The conclusions all point in the same direction: as in Kirtlington, when badgers are around, hedgehogs are scarce. Which is a problem, because badger numbers in Britain expanded throughout the twentieth century, accelerated by the provision of legal protection in the 1970s and 1990s. Between two national

---

* These surveys were run by the People's Trust for Endangered Species and the British Hedgehog Preservation Society. They are both wonderful organizations, but no matter how many times I hear 'British Hedgehog Preservation Society' I still end up with visions of Union-Jack-branded jars stuffed with pickled insectivores. That might just be me. But you can rest assured that the BHPS definitely does *not* go in for that sort of thing. Not even in private.

badger surveys in Great Britain in the 1980s and 1990s, the number of badger social groups recorded increased by 24 per cent. And a follow-up survey of England and Wales in the 2010s showed that in the twenty-five years since the 1980s survey, the number of badger social groups recorded in England had approximately doubled. The consequences for hedgehogs appear to have been concomitantly dire.

'Aha!' A plumply dashing figure in a tweed jacket and red chinos sets down his glass of whisky and bounces to his feet. 'Geddoff, here. Major Geddoff. Well, this has been quite the fandango, but it sounds like we're finally on the right track, eh? Tommy Brock, well, well. It's fair to say we've a bit of a history, no love lost, that sort of caper. Isn't that right, Tommy, old chap?'

Above the jovial smile the Major's eyes glitter. Tommy Brock scowls in return.

'Not my fault about your cows,' says Tommy Brock.

'Well, that's just the thing, isn't it? My tenant farmers would very much beg to differ. Think you've been spreading some foul pestilence about. Think, all being equal, they'd like to see the back of you, quite frankly. But TB in the fields is one thing and this is quite another. Murdering hedgehogs, is it, Tommy? That what you chaps get up to when you're peckish, eh?'

Tommy Brock snarls as Major Geddoff turns to the Detective.

'I think we've heard enough, don't you, Detective? Your bailiwick entirely, of course, but it seems the evidence is conclusive. And of course it's quite obvious what needs to be done.'

'Is it?' says the Detective. 'Could you enlighten me, Major?'

'Of course. What I'm suggesting, Detective, is that some of my good fellows could deal with the likes of old Tommy on a permanent basis.' The Major's smile turns wolfish. 'A bit of a cull never hurts, does it? Trim off some surplus, put things back in their proper place. Balance the books. And by the sounds of it we'd be doing your hedgehogs quite the favour. Something of a win–win, wouldn't you say?'

Badger culls are an issue that divides Britain. Opposing views are held passionately, and with the diamond-hard conviction that the one being held is the right one. The whole enterprise is what the term 'hot mess' was coined to describe, especially for those of us who would like policies that affect wildlife to be rational, effective and based on good science. For me the badger-cull story is an excellent example of what happens when they are not.

I should be upfront about my position, here. I adore badgers. I've been privileged to see a few up close and they are wonderful. My research group in Oxford runs annual badger censuses in a local woodland, and I have often taken part. It involves trapping them, examining them, marking them and letting them go, a process made simpler by the badgers' fetish for peanuts soaked in syrup.* Set a cage trap with some of those, and (vagaries of weather, badgers' moods etc. notwithstanding) you have a pretty good chance of catching one. And the whole process is great fun. It's also fascinating to be able to get up close to the badgers while they're being inspected and measured under anaesthetic. You get to marvel at their musculature, and their teeth, which under no circumstances

---

* Despite the fact that they appear not to be able to digest them. Which turns out to be quite handy. If you've ever lain awake at night wondering how one might go about establishing the exact limits of a badger's range (and I know you have, you devil), one way is to mix some peanuts with syrup and a handful of coloured plastic grains. Dump the foul concoction next to a badger sett and it will quickly be eaten. What goes in has to come out, in this case in badgers' latrines – little scraped troughs, often left at the edges of their territory, into which they defecate. So if you've baited a few setts with different colours, you can wait a day or so, then head into the woods to go latrine spotting. You'll find that the badgers have handily highlighted their boundaries in colour-coded poo. Gotta love ecology.

would you try examining if they were awake.* And letting them go is brilliant, seeing their big hairy bottoms galumphing off through the nettles. But I could never really shake the feeling that although the trapping was for science and conservation there was something . . . undignified about it. I never enjoyed the sight of a badger in a cage trap. They look unhappy. They stare at the ground, unmoving, waiting for it to be over.

And I tried hard to watch badgers in the wild. I spent multiple fruitless evenings parked, unmoving, next to a badger sett, often in the pouring rain. Some folks get to watch cubs frolicking, adults snuggling, rolling, play-fighting, the works. I got wet. And the one and only time I ever met a free-ranging wild badger, I wasn't intending to. It was a spring evening and I'd gone for a walk up through some woods. There's a nice spot, with a view down the hill to a reservoir, and I'd stopped

---

* You can also, if you feel like it, watch samples of putty-like material being scooped with spatulas from their sub-caudal glands (which are next to the anus, so some care is advisable) before being colour-matched against the brown–cream section of a Dulux paint chart. Yes. Really. The sub-caudal gland is used for scent marking, and the colour and composition of the secretions vary with body condition, sex and age, reproductive status and social group. It really packs a lot of information. It's kind of like Tinder, but the swiping is messier.

to enjoy it when something started rustling around up ahead. I did my usual freeze-and-pretend-I'm-Attenborough routine. And a couple of rustles later an enormous badger found itself peering myopically at my left boot. It hesitated, then inched forwards. It gave my foot a sniff. It blinked. It sniffed again. Then it did the most magnificent badger double-take. Its expression could only be described as 'Oh, holy crap'. It flung its foreclaws up and wheeled away, turning tail and huffing off through the woods. A running badger looks like it's made of rolls of sleek, muddy-haired fat. But they really shift. It was gone in a receding series of crashes.

It was such a stonking great honour to have been that close and had that interaction, however fleeting, that when I read that badger numbers are rising I can only feel this to be a good thing. It means they're rebounding from a population dip that – in common with most mammalian conservation issues – may well have had its roots in something nasty humans recently stopped doing. And what I think of when I hear the word 'badger' is loveliness. So while I may have given the impression that I was setting Tommy up as a villain, I have to ask: what has the guy really done? He's eaten some hedge-hogs. Fine. Lots of animals eat lots of other animals. Everyone loves lions and tigers and bears (oh my). We thrill at their

magnificence, and the spectacle of their stature and nobility –
embodied within which is the tacit appreciation that these are
animals powerful enough to take you to the cleaners if they
wished.* The magnificence is earned through their capacity
for killing animals and, occasionally, people.† We humans are
horribly and inconsistently judgemental about this. Hedgehog

---

* But which, of course, they wouldn't because they would naturally
recognize something in you that was special, and you would earn their
trust to form a companionship based on mutual love and respect. Hah.
Not likely. One of my colleagues used to tell a story about a couple of
lion worshippers who broke into a lion enclosure. (No, I had no idea
people worshipped lions either, but I'm willing to believe it.) They
found a sleeping lion and laid a wreath on its head. The lion woke up,
pawed the wreath off, and went back to sleep. Not taking the hint, they
picked up the wreath, and placed it back on the lion . . . which woke
up, killed one of the worshippers, took the wreath off, then went back
to sleep. Wild animals do not think the same way as domestic animals,
and we *really* need to get that into our heads.

† At which point they rather quickly stop being quite so revered, and
end up being variously stabbed, shot and otherwise disposed of. It's
quite telling that some of the unfortunate communities who live
alongside homicidal lions, for example, consider those lions to have
been possessed by evil sprits. Those are the sorts of mental contortions
we indulge in when seeking to make sense of a world in which
humans are a bit lower down the food chain than we'd like to be.

lovers may be incensed by badgers eating hedgehogs, but gamekeepers are incensed when hedgehogs eat the eggs of their (often non-native) game birds. Eating other animals in general doesn't make you bad, but eating somebody's favourite animal can be enough to get you culled.

On the subject of culling, I should also state my position. I have killed animals; I detested doing it and I hate having done it. But I would probably do it again if I felt the justification was sufficiently strong. And for me a solid justification is the conservation of species, if evidence-based. For example, we cannot ensure the survival of our native water voles in the UK while invasive American mink remain at large; and so, while I admire mink greatly, I wish for them to be removed from Britain because of the harm they do. We have decades of evidence that the approach is necessary. But does the same conservation imperative hold true for badgers and hedgehogs? Or are there other solid societal justifications that might warrant interventions to reduce badger numbers?

Because recently there have been some quite concerted attempts at doing just that. Before I started writing this I was not certain for how many years in the past decade or so Britain has been culling badgers or how many had been killed. When I found the answers, I was shocked. Badger culls have occurred in every year since 2013. In each one of the first years several thousand badgers were killed. But the numbers destroyed have risen dramatically, to 32,934 in 2018 and 40,892 in 2020, the last year for which we have data. The total number killed at the time of writing is 143,241. And the licences granted for 2021 included seven new English counties, requiring at least 33,045 badgers to be killed, up to a maximum of 75,930. Please remember that this is a protected species. So you would at least expect two things. First, that the justification is established beyond doubt, and the benefits to human society demonstrable and clear.* Second, that the killings are performed to the very best standards of animal welfare.

Beginning with the justification, this stems from bovine tuberculosis, and its terrible impacts on dairy herds. An outbreak of TB can require thousands of cows to be destroyed. This in turn has nightmarish impacts on individual farmers, logistically, psychologically – in having to destroy animals they have raised – and financially. Badgers are implicated because they too carry bovine TB, and it has been suggested that they act as a wildlife reservoir for the infection. Culling

---

* There wouldn't be any benefits to badger society. Nor, I suspect, many detectable ecological or conservation benefits in general.

badgers is meant to reduce significantly the likelihood of TB outbreaks in cows, and all the associated anguish. But does it?

The first thing to say is that everyone did excellent work at the outset. Between 1998 and 2006 a series of experimental culls were performed to see if culling badgers would do the job. The answer was that numbers of herd breakdowns (i.e. cows getting TB) did decrease in the areas where the culling was happening, relative to places where it wasn't. The problem was that the cull caused the risk of TB to *increase* temporarily in areas immediately surrounding the culling zones. That probably happened because the remaining badgers found their former social structures literally shot to pieces and went roaming in response, spreading TB around.* The experimental trials concluded that five years of culling would result in an overall reduction of only 3–21 per cent in herd breakdowns. Gains that low suggest that the majority of the TB cases are nothing to do with badgers, and so it becomes a fine judgement as to whether society feels there to be enough of a benefit to justify shooting protected wildlife. In 2007, the Independent Scientific Group on Cattle TB concluded: 'These

---

* This is known as the 'perturbation effect'. In a similar position *you'd* be pretty perturbed too.

results . . . suggest that badger culling is unlikely to contribute effectively to the control of cattle TB in Britain.' And that was that. On the evidence from the science, the government wisely decided not to go there.

Until 2010. By then we had a new government,* and a TB crisis that led to twenty-five thousand cattle being slaughtered. So government bodies revisited the original study and performed what is best described as 'selective sourcing' of assumptions from it. Off the back of those they proposed a new badger cull, to be performed by a licensed group of farmers and/or their agents. The licences required that enough badgers of any population were killed (70 per cent) to minimize the perturbation effect. The licences also required that the shootings did not wipe the creatures off the face of Britain, which would contravene our obligations under an international wildlife protection treaty known as the Bern Convention. How in the living heck anyone figured that they'd be able to judge numbers of dead badgers accurately as a proportion of a given population is beyond me. Counting badgers, like counting any wild mammals, is really difficult. Even changes in the weather can lead to a potential 55 per cent underestimate or 39 per cent

---

* The one, if you recall, that had 'had enough of experts'. Urgh.

overestimate of a population. It would be very, very easy to accidentally shoot only half the number of animals intended, leading to an increase in TB in cattle – or indeed to accidentally kill all of them.

Since 2013, in the face of immense public opposition, the state has granted annual licences that have resulted in hundreds of thousands of badgers being destroyed across south-western England. And the results? Well, after the first four years of culling, the incidence of bovine TB had decreased by 66 per cent and 37 per cent respectively in Gloucester and Somerset. In Dorset there was no change, but they had only been doing it there for two years. Government ministers pointed to these data as a ringing validation of their approach. But they pointed too soon. The very next year, the incidence of bovine TB in Gloucestershire skyrocketed – so that after five years of culling, it was now *higher* there than it had been at the start. Meanwhile, in Wales, where there was no badger culling, rates of TB in cattle declined dramatically.

Culling isn't the solution some people want it to be. Probably because most cases of TB in cattle don't come from badgers. Of two studies that estimated how much cattle infection is attributable to badgers, one suggested it caused between 10 and 20 per cent of TB cases, and the other suggested a figure of around 6 per cent. Similarly, of 313 culled badgers tested for TB in Cumbria, only three (less than 1 per cent) had it. A separate suite of post mortems, of nine hundred culled badgers, found that under 5 per cent had levels of TB infection that could be infectious to cows – or indeed other badgers.

To put this another way, at least 95 per cent, and plausibly more than 99 per cent, of all the badgers that have been shot probably posed no risk to cattle. The TB probably instead came from . . . (wait for it) . . . other cows. That initial drop in cattle TB incidence probably didn't stem from reduced badger numbers so much as from prompting the farms involved really to focus on the rest of their TB containment activities: all the cattle controls, improvements in the quality of TB testing and in the implementation of biosecurity. But if that were the case then you could get a similar result from not killing badgers at all. You could rather just tighten up on testing and herd management. I don't know about you, but that idea makes me feel pretty unhappy. I mean, surely we don't have to shoot wildlife just to get folks to concentrate on TB testing and biosecurity? The emerging consensus is that killing badgers isn't going to solve our TB problem, but that nobody seems to have a better idea. In the words of one marksman quoted by *Farmers Weekly*:

None of us wanted to do this, but we all feel it's necessary . . . [and that's] why I get steamy when people criticise us for what we are doing because it's the only show in town. No one has got any ideas of how to get rid of the disease any other way, apart from vaccination, which has no basis in science.

The only show in town is the ineffective and horrible show of shooting badgers. But even that statement is not entirely accurate. Tightening testing protocols is a show, and one that's likely to be effective. And vaccines *do* exist, for both badgers and cattle. Vaccinating badgers is preferable to killing them – but getting the vaccines into badgers, and then convincing landowners that doing so is effective, is proving tricky. Badger vaccination probably won't be replacing culling any time soon. The cattle vaccine, however, is more promising. It isn't currently being used mainly because some vaccinated cows give false-positive tests for TB under current testing standards, making it hard to monitor TB levels in vaccinated herds. The current quick skin test, however, is also far from perfect in other ways. It misses about 50 per cent of infections, meaning that every year tens of thousands of genuinely infected cattle are likely to be left freely mixing with their herdmates.

Let's fetch an envelope and do some sums. The highest post-mortem figures suggest that 5 per cent of the 143,241 dead badgers could have been infected with TB. As a top estimate, then, around 7,000 had TB, equating to around 1,000 infectious badgers a year being taken out of circulation across thirteen or so English counties. So about 100 a county. Now, badgers don't spend their nights dedicatedly doing deep-breathing exercises right up cows' noses,* and so the real-world

---

* Which is largely what it takes to transmit TB from a badger to a cow. In his book *The Fate of the Badger*, Richard Meyer describes an early experiment from 1975 in which ten badgers were put in a 12 × 8.5m covered yard with some calves, and kept there in undoubtedly stressful conditions for four years. As we shall see, about fifteen badgers per square kilometre would be a very high density to find in the wild. The badger density in this study equates to a hundred thousand badgers per square kilometre, all rammed up against cows that couldn't leave – which also never happens in reality. And unlike in the wild, the badgers were all infected. The result must surely have been swift transmission of TB, right? Well, to quote: 'despite the utterly unnatural, confined and contaminated conditions, in close quarters with a disproportionate number of infectious badgers, calves took at least six months to develop sensitivity to bovine tuberculin' (p. 84). The study was somehow heralded as a successful demonstration of the potential for badgers to become endemically infected and a source of infection for cows. Which is a bonkers interpretation that runs a severe risk of

decrease in TB transfer rates from these 100 removed badgers is probably negligible. Compare this with tens of thousands of infected cows potentially missed by screening and mixing with the rest of their herds in barns and fields. Stop me if this sounds stupid, but which approach has the greater potential for minimizing infection here: better testing, tighter protocols for moving cattle and on-farm biosecurity, or shooting wildlife?

Anyway, an alternative TB test does exist. It started being trialled in 2021 and, if approved, may mean that we can get on and vaccinate cows. But, of course, as the trials plod forwards we still have culls scheduled until 2025, meaning another three hundred thousand or so badgers could legitimately be shot – to nobody's benefit.

Before we get back to the comparatively light topic of hedgehog murders, a final point is that current badger culling methods are very probably a source of substantial suffering. I say 'probably', because nobody, now, is monitoring. In 2013

---

being seen, in retrospect, as cynically manipulative. The daily potential infection risk was clearly tiny, even in this ridiculous setup. Under normal badger densities (which are ten thousand times lower than in this study) it must be very, very, very small indeed.

the government set up an independent panel to assess 'controlled shooting' as a culling method. 'Controlled shooting' means dispensing with the difficulties of cage-trapping badgers before shooting them and instead shooting badgers on sight from a far greater distance. It's simpler and quicker – but, of course, makes it a lot more likely that someone will miss a bit and really make a mess of an unsuspecting badger. In 2014 the independent panel concluded that 'between 7.4 per cent and 22.8 per cent of badgers that were shot at were still alive after 5 min and therefore were at risk of experiencing marked pain. We are concerned at the potential for suffering that these figures imply.' They recommended that the forthcoming culls should be rigorously monitored, to refine the technique. The government's apparent response to these concerns was to disband the panel in 2014, leaving all operations since with little oversight. The proportion of badgers shot by controlled shooting has been increased from approximately 50 per cent in 2014 to 77 per cent in 2020. Because even though it's probably condemning thousands of sentient animals to die in terrible pain every year, it's . . . well, it's easier.

I have nothing but sympathy for landowners who experience herd breakdowns. I can't imagine the trauma of having to destroy your animals. And I completely understand the farming community's frustration and desire to do something. I also get that they are completely fed up at being vilified for taking what they perceive to be the only available route out of the situation. Very few people really want to be slaughtering wildlife, but they genuinely feel it's their only option. But these landowners have been badly served by a mule-headed governmental approach that continues to take the popular, crowd-pleasing route, rather than focusing on evidence-led measures that might actually solve the issue. Killing badgers cannot and will not eradicate bovine TB, or even lower its incidence significantly. There has been a colossal failure of management and communication, leading to entrenched positions and conflict. And while the humans argue, wildlife continues to be unnecessarily shot.

Right. Where were we? Oh yes. As Major Geddoff smirkingly remarked, there does seem to be the potential for a single silver lining to the whole badger-cull debacle. Could it have reversed the hedgehog's circumstances? Such a finding would put beyond question that surging badger numbers were indeed driving hedgehogs towards extinction. But actually the only evidence we have is one academic study from 2014. The researchers surveyed hedgehogs during the initial badger-cull trials, in multiple sites across four different counties. Each site comprised nine pasture fields within 1km of a village, and three amenity grasslands at village edges. Over four to six years they searched for hedgehogs using spotlights, to get a count of how many individuals there were in each field. The result seems positive, but muted. In the pasture fields they found a grand total of twelve hedgehogs over the entire experiment. Lots of empty fields near villages stayed empty. Not much of use there. In the amenity grassland in culling zones, over six or so years, hedgehog densities more than doubled, from one hedgehog per hectare to about two and a half hedgehogs per hectare. This doubling didn't happen at the non-culling sites. That was an effect, certainly, but the authors couldn't be entirely sure if the doubling of hedgehog sightings meant that the hedgehogs were more numerous or simply venturing further from the village. Even if the former was true, the wider picture is not entirely of a joyful rebounding, with badger-freed hedgehogs spilling out into the countryside in some sort of high-school musical number. At best this is an increase seen only in the grasslands immediately surrounding villages. Whether, over time, it could become more is unknown.

Did you ever get the feeling that something, somewhere isn't quite adding up? The badger-versus-hedgehog relationship

seems neat – badger numbers surged, hedgehogs declined –
and there is a clear mechanism by which badgers might
influence the hedgehogs' distribution and numbers. But the
same was true of the cars, if you recall.* And while it remains
true that the presence of badgers is negatively associated with
the presence of hedgehogs, we run into a few snags when trying to use this observation to pin the decline on Tommy Brock.
A negative association is *not* the same as saying that the existence of badgers in a given area guarantees the absence of
hedgehogs. A study I cited above found that without badgers
29 per cent of sites had hedgehogs, versus 17 per cent with
them. Two aspects of those statistics should give us pause. The
first is that the vast majority of badger-free rural sites (71 per
cent) didn't have any hedgehogs, *even though there were
no badgers*. So something else made them unsuitable for

---

* Interesting, isn't it, that some folks are calling for badgers to be shot
as a conservation measure while car numbers have clearly risen, and
also definitely kill hedgehogs, but nobody is busily culling cars, or
even seriously attempting to put in place measures to limit their
effects. Which is unfortunate, because a car cull would also benefit the
large proportion of British wildlife for which attempting to move about
the country now means finishing up as a two-dimensional Damien
Hirst installation entitled 'Hairclump on Asphalt'.

hedgehogs. The second is that hedgehogs were found at fifty-five sites, and badgers were present at just under half of those (49 per cent). So at half the sites, badgers and hedgehogs were coexisting within the same square kilometre.

An area containing one or two badgers is rather different than an all-out standing-room-only stripey badger-fest. So studies looking at densities (rather than only presence) are probably the way forwards. The snag is that all the studies that have tried to show the effects of badger density on hedgehogs have used numbers of badger setts as a proxy for badger abundance – the logic being that more setts means more badgers. But that might not actually be true. The number of badgers in a given social group can vary between three and eight. Two small setts might hold fewer badgers than one large one, so it's not a foolproof measure. I found only one very recent study that examined badgers and hedgehogs using locally derived density estimates for both (obtained using camera traps). That study discovered that the two species could share an area until there were fifteen badgers or more per square kilometre. That's a lot of badgers. The vast majority of sites had somewhere between two and eight per square kilometre. And when the study examined correlates for

hedgehog densities, badgers were not the most important factor. Far more important was the distance from a given locality
to buildings. Again, the hedgehogs clung to the human habitations, the badgers avoided them.

We have a problem. Early in this chapter we established
that hedgehogs like to be around buildings and grassy amenity areas, and that badgers don't. This observation could easily
lead us to conclude that badgers drive hedgehogs out of the
countryside and towards the refuge of buildings. And that
might be true. But what if it isn't? If hedgehogs didn't give two
hoots about badgers, but couldn't live in the wider countryside for some other reason, we'd see much the same pattern.
So the answer to our hedgehog conservation riddle is maybe
not as simple as 'badger numbers have risen and hedgehog
numbers have fallen'.* There may be hidden, mediating and
co-occurring factors at play in our countryside. Badgers almost
certainly don't make life easier for hedgehogs, and certainly
do kill and eat them, but we still have no proof that they

---

* The badger issue, you see, isn't black and white. (Joke credit goes to
Hugh Warwick, hedgehog guru. As should any remonstrations from
the pun-intolerant.)

are the ultimate root of the problem. That may yet lie elsewhere . . .

Tommy Brock rises to his feet. His frame is imposing in the half-light. It's dim in his corner of the library, but the gloom cannot hide his thick chest and powerful forearms. Tommy peers at the occupants of the library, then growls at the Major.

'*Have you said everything you wish?*'

Major Geddoff shrinks back a little. He snatches up his whisky, and takes a hasty swallow. Then he pulls himself together, and meets Tommy Brock's eyes.

'*Well, what more needs to be said, Tommy?*'

He almost pulls off the bravado. Almost. But he sits too hastily, and the glass rattles as he places it on the tabletop.

'*Plenty,*' *says Tommy.* '*Plenty about me and hedge-pigs. Plenty about me and you.*' *He lowers his head, and takes a breath. And when he raises it again, his gaze is penetrating.* '*My kind have delved earth since times forgotten. Before machines and roads. Before bricks and books. Before cows and ploughs. Before you knew these shores existed. And in all that time we lived with the hedge-pigs.*' *He raises his arms in a gesture almost of supplication.* '*We live now as we lived then. Only now do the pigs vanish, and you say it was us that did it. How so?*' *The growl in his voice intensifies.* '*We* have not changed. The lands changed. I don't know the fields of my cub-hood, not no more. When I roam it's not through the woods and fields of my ancestors. I tread poorer earth.' His voice is thick. 'Not made poorer by me. You sullied our territories, changed them quick, so they can't take us and the pigs together. Not my fault. Yours. Your fault. And yet you set your hopes on my destruction.'

The room is silent. His gaze sweeps the crowd, fierce, one more time. And then his head drops and his shoulders slump.

'I have said everything I wish to,' says Tommy Brock. And he hunkers down, brooding, back in his seat.

'Well.' The Detective raises an eyebrow at Major Geddoff. 'The gentleman raises an interesting point, Major. Do you have a response that you wish to share?'

CHAPTER 4

Coming a Cropper (but Ploughing on Regardless)

Have you ever wondered why, why the crime rate . . . is so low, yet the accident rate is so high?

NICHOLAS ANGEL,
Hot Fuzz

THE DUNGHILL WAS SOMETHING ELSE, AN IMMENSE PILE of sheep faeces and straw, right on the roadside. It was nothing too unusual for a pastoral farm, sure, but the scale was spectacular. It must have been a full storey high.* And this particular aggregation of steaming agricultural by-product was distinguished by a number of intriguing features. One of these was that there always seemed to be hedgehogs bustling around it. And this observation led hedgehog researcher Lauren Moore – whom we met in chapter 2 and in whose study site the pile was situated – to go and ask the landowner if he had any particular objection to her having a good rummage around inside. This was not a question he necessarily expected, but she didn't look obviously unwell and was carrying a

---

* Indeed, yes. And I know what you're thinking: *Please, oh please, tell me more about this enormous mound of excrement.* Well, rest assured, we'll be immersed in more manure before you can say 'defecation'.

bunch of radio-tracking equipment, so he said 'yes'. And that, ladies and gentlemen, is how Lauren ended up spending the best part of an hour up to her knees in a tottering sheep midden.

It was worth it. Because the dunghill was stuffed full of hedgehogs. They were using it for nesting, sometimes within a metre of one another. Any hedgehog researcher will tell you that nesting so closely is highly unusual, and that's testament to what an amazing hedgehog resource such piles represent. They are brilliantly insulated and the various exothermic breakdown processes will make them cosily centrally heated. Add to this their potential as a haven for various edible insects and you're looking at a slightly whiffy hedgehog paradise. Even the location was good. The surrounding fields were at the bottom of a village, and formed the epicentre of all the local hedgehog activity. Lauren's hedgehogs had found a nice warm nesting place right where they wanted to be. They had won life's lottery . . .

. . . right up until the day the whole heap was picked up and carted off. The removal was no doubt performed by some enormous piece of farm machinery. And that's important, because if the stack had been loaded piecemeal by people

with pitchforks the hedgehogs would probably have been dis-
interred and run away. As it was, Lauren never saw any of them
again. Were they killed or injured during the removal? Were
they able to survive long enough to make new homes wherever it was they were transported to? Nobody knows. But it's a
fair bet that a lot of them died.

Many of the farms where Lauren worked had similar piles,
and from time to time those too would disappear overnight.
Hedgehogs almost certainly disappeared with them. Because
what the hedgehogs perceived as safe, cosy nests were only
ever intended by the farmers to act as temporary poo-storage.
A simple disconnect between human intention and hedgehog
instinct had the effect of turning each of those dunghills into
a rather lethal ecological trap. Nobody's fault, but the outcome
for the hedgehogs was dire.

Dire accidental outcomes for hedgehogs have become an
increasingly common feature of our agricultural landscapes.
An example of a more subtle trap is that some of the best
hedges on Lauren's sites were right on the road verge. (As
indeed was the dung pile.) This road was where Lauren had
been studying the effects of traffic on hedgehog populations, and where she had found nearly all her hedgehog

traffic casualties. Many hedgehogs nested there, just metres from the danger.* There weren't so many nesting in the farms' other hedges, presumably because the hedges were managed differently in some way and were consequently less suitable. So an unexpected knock-on consequence of differences in hedgerow management funnelled hedgehog activity towards a road accident black spot. And that, of course, could have dire implications for the population's death rate.

These are anecdotes. They don't make for easy generalizations. We cannot know how common disappearing dung-heaps are across Britain, or how many hedgehogs are annually spirited away to an uncertain fate. We don't have data on whether road-verge hedges are typically different from other farm hedges and so typically perceived by hedgehogs to be better. But even if these are mere unfortunate one-offs, the issues they raise are symptomatic of forces that continue to shape our agricultural landscapes, forces inextricably linked with industrialization and mechanization, forces which have collectively been catastrophic for hedgehogs.

---

* Blearily getting out of the wrong side of bed and into the path of something speedy wouldn't be the best start to an evening's activities.

There is a clue in the name 'hedgehog'. It isn't meant to be ironic. It isn't a clever joke.* These are snuffling animals that superficially resemble small spiny pigs, and tend to be found in and around hedges. And especially for farmland hedgehogs, hedges are vitally important. Study after study has shown that although hedgerow makes up only a tiny fraction of the overall area of a typical hedgehog's range, that tiny fraction is where the hedgehogs opt to spend most of their time. Species-rich hedgerows interspersed with trees are excellent environments for hedgehog-munchable invertebrates, which can be handily hoovered up from the habitats that cling to hedge bases. A good brambly or rosy base to a hedge also provides some great hedgehog nesting sites, for both summer nests and winter hibernation. Mature trees in hedges likewise

---

* Unlike 'Hedgehogs – why can't they just share the hedge?', which won Dan Antopolski the funniest joke of the Edinburgh Fringe award in 2009. It's a great one-liner. And was promptly ripped off by a load of folks who owned T-shirt printing businesses. And their designs in turn got copied by other vendors, who incorporated elements into their own T-shirts, and mugs, and tote bags, and cushions, until a simple internet search causes all sorts of unbelievable joke-bearing tat to come spilling off the screen and into your brain. If only a fraction of all this feverish industry were somehow diverted into saving actual hedgehogs, or indeed laying hedges, we'd have things sorted in short order.

provide nesting material, as well as being wonderful for keeping up those all-important invertebrate numbers. So that's food and shelter covered. And when moving around, hedgehogs often follow linear features, especially when dispersing – and in this role hedges at field margins provide thoroughfares that connect hedgehog populations. Hedges are also warmer than the surrounding landscape, acting as windbreaks with their own microclimates. One study recorded the average temperature at night as 10.7°C in the middle of arable fields, but 11.4°C in the hedgerows. The difference is slight, yes, but to a small and not particularly fluffy insectivore any additional warmth, over hours, days and weeks, might well make the energetic difference between survival and hypothermia. And, of course, we can add to all these benefits the fact that stands of dense vegetation in general, and hedges in particular, provide refuge for hedgehogs away from predation by badgers and foxes.*

---

* I haven't spoken much about foxes. They can predate upon hedgehogs, especially juveniles. They probably can't do a lot to get at most adults, if properly curled, but will definitely try their luck waiting it out and snapping at any protruding legs. Most predation by foxes seems to happen infrequently enough for them to be added to the category of 'general risks to a hedgehog' rather than a major source of mortality in the way that badgers are.

A dense, thick clump of tough, interwoven and preferably thorny plants, with a few small holes to disappear into, may well frustrate the heck out of a hungry badger. A hedge like that would provide a hedgehog with a happy feeling of safety as it goes about its business. And, as we have seen, with badgers about, hedgehogs stick tight to hedges.

Hedges are not just for hedgehogs, of course. For a lot of wildlife, farm fields may as well be a desert. Hedges are life-giving tendrils of semi-natural habitat weaving around the margins of relatively barren fields. They perform vital ecological functions. Like hedgehogs, lots of flora and fauna live in them – but also need them to connect habitat patches together, especially mobile species that use them as highways. The likelihood of a given stand of woodland being occupied by wood mice and bank voles gets lower as you get further from the next nearest woodland patch (because it becomes quite a trek), but higher again the more extensive the surrounding hedgerow. Both species use hedges to disperse, and a nice network of hedges means that suitable woodlands can be reached and colonized, making the whole of the wider population more robust. Similarly, you are more likely to find common toads on farmland that has a lot of woodlands and hedgerows, and less likely to find them when there are proportionally more crops. It works for flying mammals too. The amount of bat activity, specifically of pipistrelle and serotine bats, increases with the amount of linear features (i.e. hedges and tree lines) you have in a landscape. I could go on, listing plants, invertebrates, birds and mammals for which similar trends apply, but the overall message is simple: hedges on farmland are incredibly important for wildlife. And no species relies on them more than hedgehogs. Food, warmth, nests, protection, navigation: everything a hedgehog needs to have a good time comes from a hedge. Without them, life for a farm hog would be unpleasant in the extreme.*

All of which makes the events that befell post-war British farmland something of a shame.† Published estimates of the total length of British hedgerow from the 1940s vary, but there was something like one million kilometres of them. By

---

* And quite short.

† Note: deliberate understatement. There are only so many times an author can use the word 'catastrophe' without the reader wondering if they're not getting a bit hysterical and might benefit from a nice lie down. But the word 'catastrophe' actually doesn't come close to describing the consequences of post-war agricultural intensification for a staggering array of British wildlife.

1990, that total had been reduced to 400,000km, and has pretty much stayed around that figure since. In forty years, Britain removed enough hedgerow to wrap around the circumference of the Earth about fifteen times.* The speed of removal was incredible. Between 1984 and 1990, for example, 121,000km (22 per cent of the then-existing hedgerow stock) was grubbed out. The hurry during those particular years seems ironically to have resulted from the government considering plans to protect hedges. Farmers redoubled their removal efforts before they got prevented by any new legislation. Because removing hedges was seen as imperative.

---

* Depending on the initial estimate used and taking the Earth's circumference to be about 40,000km or so. As units of measurement go, 'the circumference of the Earth' is right up there with 'football pitches' and 'Wales', but it is rather difficult to find a handy visualization of just how massive 600,000km is. As another attempt, that estimate of hedgerows removed would also get you to the moon and most of the way back, if you could figure out a way to make it all stand up vertically. And to give you an idea of how incredibly distant the moon is, if you could stack all the planets of the solar system one after the next in a line, they would easily fit between the Earth and the moon.

The imperative arose from mechanization, itself stemming from Britain's desire to become more self-sufficient in food. There was a huge drive to increase field sizes, and (literally) reap the benefits of reduced manpower and improved efficiency. And the agronomic gains are undeniable. In 1970 cereal cutters left about 2–3 per cent of the harvestable crop on the field. These days acceptable losses are eight to twelve times smaller – less than 0.25 per cent of the crop gets left behind. But mechanization was expensive, requiring substantial upfront investment. The costs led to farms becoming larger in scale but fewer in number, as smaller farms were subsumed into bigger ones, and more likely to specialize in either livestock or arable crops. The results of that can be read in our landscapes. These days whole counties are dominated by either pastoral or arable farms, with little mixing of the two. In pastoral areas, fields are about 70 per cent larger than in the 1960s, but in arable areas, where livestock-proof field boundaries aren't needed, fields have more than doubled in size, from an average of 6.5 hectares to 16 hectares. British counties with mainly arable farms now have a density of hedgerows that is only about a fifth to a third of those found in pastoral counties – which may well explain why hedgehogs don't seem to like arable land very much.

We yanked out hundreds of thousands of kilometres of prime hedgehog habitat. And the stuff left isn't necessarily in great condition. In 2007 the Countryside Survey found that just under half (48 per cent) of managed hedgerows were in good structural condition. And if the criteria for condition were extended to include the width of undisturbed ground surrounding the hedge (i.e. a measure of how close to the hedge a field is cropped or grazed), only 31 per cent of hedgerows are well managed.

To continue the gloom-mongering, agricultural intensification also came packaged with quite a commitment to spraying pesticides and herbicides. Taking pesticides as an example, before 1930 these were mostly preparations of lime, copper or sulphur. By 1955, thirty-seven different compounds had been approved. By 1970 this was 136, and by 1997 344. And the total area sprayed every year in England and Wales has increased from less than 500,000 hectares in 1970 to three million hectares by the year 2000.* All of those chemicals can damage the abundance and diversity of farmland invertebrate populations, and in so doing decrease the hedgehogs' food supply.

---

* I don't know how many football pitches that is. I'm not going there.

And not only the hedgehogs'. Populations of many British farmland bird species have declined, and the loss of invertebrates is heavily implicated. Between 1970 and 1990 the geographical range occupied by twenty-four bird species (of twenty-eight studied) contracted, and fifteen species (of eighteen studied) declined in abundance. In another study, population sizes of eleven (of thirteen studied) specialist farmland birds were shown to have approximately halved between 1968 and 1995. Broadly similar declines have been recorded for both insects and spiders, which prompted researchers to examine trends in birds and arthropods* on farmland. They concluded that changes in bird numbers were likely to be linked to farming practices at least partially because of those practices' effects on farmland invertebrates. To put it another way, invertebrates declined, and invertebrate-eating birds also declined. And this wasn't coincidental. Yet again, arable farms were the worst affected. Bird densities are now highest in mixed farmland, followed by pastoral farmland, and lowest in arable landscapes, owing to lower invertebrate and plant food

---

* Arthropods are basically any invertebrate with jointed limbs. Scuttley things like insects and spiders, rather than slithery things like worms and slugs.

resources. Song thrushes have declined in Britain in part because they have increasingly been unable to source enough invertebrates in summer, a result of fast-drying arable soils coupled with a lack of alternative grasslands and woodlands to forage in. Everything has conspired together, from the heavy machinery that causes soil compaction (bad for soil invertebrates) to the usage of pesticides that affects invertebrate availability and the loss of mosaics of different habitats, as our farm landscapes have been simplified and sanitized. It has all contributed to a sustained loss of farmland biodiversity.

It is hard to disentangle the respective impacts of individual changes because everything happened at once and nobody was monitoring. And we don't know what the effect on hedgehogs was. We have no data showing *before* and *after*. And so nothing is nailed-on or proven. But sometimes you don't need it to be. The destruction of any species' food and shelter on that scale can only be disastrous. If somebody gave you the option of being a hedge-dwelling, invertebrate-eating animal living through the past few decades, you wouldn't be in a hurry to accept.* Farmland hedgehogs have been left colder

---

* Okay, that's a bad example. I'm not sure anyone would opt to be a hedge-dwelling invertebrate-eater at the best of times. Let's try a different

and hungrier, with nowhere to sleep and no safe way to navigate, exposed to predation and competition for food from badgers, and probably feeling that life in general used to be a whole lot better, thank you oh so very much. And hedgehogs are just one species, representative of a whole host of plants and animals for which agricultural intensification in general, and hedgerow removal in particular, has been devastating. At least half of our hedgerows have gone, and with them went a lot of our wildlife.

If you were to judge the farming community solely on the outcome of these actions, you would assume that farmers tend to view wildlife as an inconvenience at best, to be disposed of in pursuit of food production. But that is actually far from how farmers typically see their role. In two questionnaire surveys in 1981 and 1998 – with responses from 859 and 451 farmers, respectively – farmers were asked to assess their level of interest in wildlife (uninterested, quite interested or very interested). In the first survey, 40 per cent said they were very interested, rising to 62 per cent in the second. Only 3.7 per

---

approach. Given the option of being a hedge-dwelling invertebrate-eater on a farm in the 1930s versus a hedge-dwelling invertebrate-eater on a farm in the 1990s, it's a no-brainer.

cent and 0.7 per cent said they were uninterested. And in both surveys, over 95 per cent of all farmers said they considered themselves to be primarily responsible for the countryside. In response to the hypothetical question whether they would be willing to create wildlife refuges on their land if subsidies were made available, 66.2 per cent in the first survey said that they would, and 91.9 per cent in the second. These data chime with my own experience of the landowners I've worked with. They've all been terrific, proud of their farms and keen to support biodiversity. They see themselves as custodians of the landscape and protectors of the species that share it. And many work very hard indeed, both in general and for wildlife.

We have a disconnect between the willingness of farmers to foster wildlife and the highly destructive collective impacts caused by agricultural intensification on individual farms. This shouldn't be a surprise. There is nearly always a gap between people's intentions and their actions where the environment is concerned. We all want to behave sustainably, but few of us truly manage it, largely because of the *many* barriers that stand in our way. Perhaps we don't have enough information to predict the consequences of a given decision (a knowledge barrier). Or perhaps we have to take a damaging option because there are no other alternatives (a structural barrier). Or perhaps the options are too expensive or would take too much time (a financial barrier); or perhaps there are uncomfortable social consequences to going against established norms (a social barrier). At various points all of these will have influenced the behaviour of landowners. And the upshot is that in the 1981 survey there was no link whatsoever between how interested in wildlife farmers said they were and the length of hedgerow they'd removed. In the 1998 survey the farmers more interested in wildlife did remove slightly less hedgerow, but the difference was negligible. Everyone at that time was ripping out hedges, and there were highly persuasive agronomic reasons for doing so (83–87 per cent of farmers said they removed hedgerows to improve efficiency), and little alternative if farms were to stay competitive. These reasons, probably coupled with simply not really seeing the harm, resulted in farmers acting in ways that ultimately ran counter to their values. With few economic incentives to retain hedgerows, and overwhelming economic and agronomic benefits to getting rid of them, the consequence was entirely predictable.

I have one more point to make here, and it's one that might seem a bit esoteric – but it has profound and real consequences. It's about social norms and tidiness. We all assume that something that looks well tended must also be well managed. It's as true of our farms as it is of our homes, gardens and parks. Many farmers believe that a tidy, clean agricultural landscape is a sign of a 'good' farmer. Tenant farmers are often required to keep hedges within set widths and heights, and in the above surveys 'tidiness' was frequently mentioned as a good reason for removing hedgerows. Also, the aesthetics of fields are felt to reflect upon not only a farm's economic status but also a farmer's social position. In the spirit of friendly competition, many farmers are more than willing to take the mickey out of each other's perceived mistakes. The desire to be seen to be running a tight ship is deeply rooted, and has resulted in nice, neat agricultural landscapes. The problem is that nearly every place that is good for biodiversity shares one common feature: it isn't neat.

And this brings us back to the dunghill story. The dunghill removal wasn't a one-off. It was something that happens on a well-run, tidy farm. Which makes it the kind of accident that happens all the time, everywhere, a consequence of an evolving way of doing business that is increasingly incompatible with retaining wildlife.

Nobody in our agricultural lands set out to murder hedgehogs. But if hedgehog murder *had* been the goal, and the killers had been determined to use the most ruthless and effective tactics to achieve it, the methods and end result would have looked pretty similar. We optimized practices for food production and, as a by-product, haemorrhaged wildlife.

The murder rate may indeed have been low. But the accident rate was, and remains, sky-high.

Major Geddoff stares down into his whisky. 'My tenants are good chaps,' he says. 'I won't have you accusing them of harming animals. Except for vermin.' And here he glares at Tommy Brock. But his bounce and swagger have gone. Ice chinks in his glass as he looks up. 'Listen,' he says, 'there's something in what you say. I remember the days of grubbing out hedges, and I can't say I'd do it again. But the times were different. It was that or be uncompetitive. Farming is a business. We make food, and make it cheap, and if there isn't enough, people go hungry. It's hard graft, slim margins.'

'I understand,' says the Detective, softly.

'And listen,' says Major Geddoff. 'It's in the past anyhow. We still do have hedges, you know, and there are all these newfangled schemes to put in grassy bits and whatnot. That must be doing some good, wouldn't you think?' He sits back. 'My lads are modern farmers, sharp as they come, good on their subsidies. I can't visit

without falling over some new patch of wildflowers or other.' And
with that thought Major Geddoff starts looking happier. 'Oh yes,' he
says, 'I'd be surprised if my farms weren't still heaving with
hedgehogs.'

I'll admit to having been spoilt in the early days of my field
ecology career. I worked in fenlands and on rivers, habitats
that are never still, always humming, bustling, striving. Later
on I did work on an array of farms, but again I was down by
the river, in the lush, running habitats. And so when I visited
some dry bits of a few farms with Carly, my student studying
hedgehogs, I was dismayed. The fields were chilly and wind-
swept, over-large, level and bare. Apart from the occasional
tree, there was little to draw the eye upwards. Apart from the
hedges, I couldn't imagine where wild animals would be hiding. And yet we were there for the wildlife.

Carly had a plan. She wanted to study how different management options (as provided under various government
agri-environment schemes) might benefit hedgehog populations. So we located six farms, representing three different
ways of doing things. Two had the type of arable fields found
across Britain, cropped up to the hedges (these were the ones
I visited). Four farms had an additional 4–6m of grassy

margin alongside each hedge, and of those, two were farmed organically, with no herbicides or pesticides. The grassy margins should provide good food and shelter for hedgehogs and organic cultivation would offer a further boost, because it didn't involve spraying the hedgehog food half to death. The working hypothesis was that we should record, on each farm, a difference in numbers of hedgehogs, how they moved about the landscape, their body condition, and how they divided their time between different activities. Overall the experiment would cover about 6,000 hectares of farmland, and the results would tell us something about how to improve farmland for hedgehogs. A nice, robust strategy for the first year of Carly's PhD.

But first she needed hedgehogs to track. In spring 2012 I helped Carly set out footprint tunnels baited with food. We positioned them at least 100m apart along the farms' hedges, and Carly checked on them every day. She found . . . nothing. Multiple thousands of hectares of prime Oxfordshire farmland yielded just one set of hedgehog footprints. A further survey of the field in which those prints occurred – a barley crop with grassy margins – turned up zilch, nada, nichts. Not one solitary additional track. Sometimes your feelings are right. The hedgehogs didn't seem to like the farms any more than I did.

We needed a backup option, and quickly, to salvage Carly's first field season. We worked on the assumption that we had missed some hedgehogs, and that the fields should, in general, be more than suitable.* And with that in mind, Carly hatched a cunning plan. A sneaky way of finding hedgehogs is to get other hedgehogs to lead you to them. While hedgehogs in general are not particularly fond of aggregating, nothing else is nearly as good at finding a female hedgehog as a male hedgehog – so one way or another, if you release and follow a hedgehog of either sex you have a good chance of encountering more of them. Carly agreed to take twelve hedgehogs from local rescue centres, animals that had overwintered and gained weight and now needed to be released into the wild. She would equip them with radio transmitters, and release them on three of the farms. They would lead us to the other hedgehogs and in the process, we hoped, make themselves at home, meaning we could get some data not only from established hedgehogs, but also from the released ones. It was, we felt, a pretty cool solution. So Carly released her rehabilitated hedgehogs and radio-tracked them diligently between 9 p.m. and

---

* Organic farms with additional grassy margins! I mean, come on, what more do they want? Picky flipping urchins.

3 a.m. for weeks. The results were sleep deprivation and 1,200 fixed hedgehog locations.

We should have expected the outcome. Of ten hedgehogs – excluding two that disappeared because their radio tags failed – eight hot-footed it across the farmland straight to the nearest village. Oh, they hung around for a few days first, constructed nests and kicked about in the hedges and margins, but most then departed pretty promptly. After a month, seven of those hedgehogs were happily making homes in assorted villages, farm gardens and allotments. One sadly got poisoned by slug pellets and had to be returned to the rescue centre. Only two hedgehogs stayed on their release farms, not nearly enough for us to be able to gain anything from studying them. And we were led to only one other hedgehog. This was a juvenile sighted in the same field where we found the original hedgehog footprint. And guess what else was unusual about that field? It backed on to a village. That juvenile was found only 10m away from someone's garden.

The reason we should have expected our hedgehogs to leave is that we were not the first to release hedgehogs and track them – not even the first in Oxfordshire, and not by a long shot. In fact, hedgehog translocation studies have yielded remarkably consistent outcomes,* with a few variations. As ever, Pat Morris pioneered, with initial releases in 1989 and 1991 of four and eight hedgehogs respectively. The four hedgehogs were released into woodland, where one died and the rest established ranges for a few weeks before two of them were picked up by the researchers and moved into a nearby field, which they both immediately left to return to woodland habitats. They seemed to like it there, and so were left there. The eight hedgehogs from the latter study were released into a mixture of hay meadows, arable land and villages. Half of them upped sticks, travelled over 2km from the release site and never returned, some settling into gardens.

In 1993 Pat Morris (with fellow hedgehog guru Hugh Warwick†) released twelve hedgehogs on to a pasture farm in

---

* Contextual definition of 'translocation': picking up an unsuspecting hedgehog and dropping it somewhere unfamiliar to see what it does. Most of these studies were either initial attempts to see if hedgehog rehabilitation could work or, later, to establish new populations with rehabilitated animals. Some were experimental to gain vital conservation information. But one can only imagine that the hedgehogs' general response was some sort of politely outraged bewilderment.

† At that time Pat's student, so possibly an apprentice guru? Guru in training?

Devon. Most stayed local, and some later died (of badger pre-dation and road traffic), but three hedgehogs quickly legged it, eventually settling amid buildings on other farms. And in 1995, Pat released thirteen hedgehogs into a garden in Jersey, close to farms and gardens. Most of the hedgehogs stayed in the area, making ample use of local gardens and rarely using any of the cropped fields.

In 1995 yet another hedgehog maester (Nigel Reeve) released twelve hedgehogs into some unoccupied woodlands in Surrey.* He aimed to test whether hedgehogs in previous studies that had dispersed did so because of overcrowding. If so, perhaps the hedgehogs would want to remain in the (empty) woodlands? They didn't. With the benefit of hind-sight, the woodland habitat may not have been entirely suitable, not least because there were three active badger setts within a 1km radius of the release point. Within a month, almost all the hedgehogs had left. With the excep-tion of three animals that died (of badger, pneumonia and

---

* Unoccupied by hedgehogs, at least. A now generally understood rule of reintroductions and translocations is that if a species is absent from a given location you need to find out why before letting more go there. There could be a good reason for the absence. And sometimes that reason has lots of teeth.

suspected road traffic, respectively), they *all* headed to human habitations. Compare these to two 'control' hedgehogs he released into already occupied urban habitats, which happily stayed put.

Woodlands themselves aren't necessarily bad for hedgehogs. In 1991 a study released hedgehogs into two sites, both a mixture of woodland and grazed pasture fields, near Oxford. One of those sites was Wytham Woods, home to many of the university's studies on birds and nearly all of my research group's studies on badgers.* At the time of the release it had no hedgehogs and a humdinger of a badger population at twenty per square kilometre. The other site, at Eynsham Park, was a very similar woodland close by, which had a thriving hedgehog population and only a few badgers (two per square kilometre). Thirty hedgehogs were released into Wytham Woods, most of which were sourced by catching hedgehogs in Eynsham Park and moving them, leaving that site empty. Into the newly vacant Eynsham Park twenty new individuals were released, this time sourced from within Oxford city and its surrounds. By the end of the musical-chairs-for-hedgehogs,

---

* Yes, you're right. In retrospect, that piece of information really doesn't bode well, does it?

two new populations had been released, one into proven hedgehog habitat and one into a full-on gnashing badger party.

The Wytham hedgehogs scattered and ran. Seven were eaten by badgers, the corpses found up to 4km apart in pasture fields and scrublands. Four were killed by cars, and one died of unknown causes. Of the remaining eighteen, all but four ended up in nearby villages, and of those four only three remained anywhere near their release point. The average distance the hedgehogs dispersed was about 2km. Of the twenty hedgehogs released into the other site, three died, but thirteen stayed put, dispersing on average less than a kilometre.*

---

* If some aspects of this ecological experiment make you feel a bit uneasy, I understand and agree. But the context is important. At the time, relatively little was known about habitat suitability, badgers and hedgehogs. The ecologist in me appreciates that the study was a very neat way to separate out the effect of badgers and woodland on a newly released population. The information derived from it has underpinned a lot of our understanding and so hugely helped hedgehog conservation. But it's a tricky balance to strike against the unfortunate outcome for some of the Wytham hedgehogs. With the benefit of hindsight, wild creatures were taken from established ranges, in areas with low numbers of predators, and transferred into

These studies demonstrate a few clear trends. Hedgehogs don't waste time: they'll leave places they don't like. Put them somewhere unsuitable and they vote with their feet. But they will stick around if they feel a new location to be up to their standards. A small proportion might move away, but generally hedgehogs seem willing to settle in good habitat. If they do decide to disperse, though, almost all of them will eventually settle in human-inhabited areas, especially village and farm gardens.

But what causes hedgehogs to perceive a given release location as unsuitable? Well, the answer probably hinges on some balance between *push factors* and possibly a *pull factor*. Push factors comprise anything that might cause a hedgehog to think 'uh-oh'. High densities of badgers would do it, as would the absence of good nesting and foraging sites. Hedgehogs probably also respond to other hedgehogs. If a place is too crowded, a hedgehog may seek somewhere calmer. Conversely, too few other hedgehogs might cause an intelligent individual to wonder why, and to try to move somewhere

---

unfamiliar territory with lots of predators. But much of the knowledge informing our retrospective viewpoint simply wasn't available then.

more popular.* And even the dumbest of brick-thick hedge-hogs would eventually twig that if they ever wanted sex again they might need somebody to do it with. So in terms of push factors, hedgehogs will be making a running assessment of the quality of food, predation risk, microclimate, nesting sites and the social situation. Pull factors are trickier, because they require hedgehogs to have an understanding of the relative benefits of other habitats elsewhere. If, for example, village hedgehogs had been taken into care, rehabilitated, and then released into farmland, they might reject it mainly because they had village gardens in mind. But this wasn't the case for most of Carly's hedgehogs, because more than half of them had never seen a human-inhabited area. And yet that is where most of them ended up. On balance, these studies suggest a general movement away from entirely rural habitats, which often seem to have been perceived as unsuitable, and towards human-inhabited areas which, when encountered, were deemed eminently suitable and settled-down in.

After Carly's hedgehog exodus, she was left trying to unpick

---

* To put this in ecologist terminology, they may use the presence or absence of conspecifics as an honest proxy indicator of environmental quality. We do love our jargon.

how food, shelter and badgers might interact to cause hedgehogs to end up in villages. To tease apart these three factors,
Carly found four near-identical study sites in which hedgehogs lived in villages surrounded by arable fields, and threw
badgers into the mix* by ensuring that two sites had badgers
and two didn't. This had been done before, of course, her
setup echoing a previous study that had radio-tracked hedgehogs to see what influence the badgers had on the way they
used the villages and fields. But Carly added an innovation.
She was going to record the hedgehogs' behaviour, habitat
choices and range sizes, and also how much energy they were
using. For a small mammal, energy budget is everything. To
paraphrase Mr Micawber from *David Copperfield*, if you
expend even slightly more energy than you ingest, the result
is misery. And if some combination of farmland and badgers
leads to poor ingestion or extra high energy expenditure, that
might explain a lot about why hedgehogs tend to go
elsewhere.

For the study Carly needed a lot of radio-tagged animals.
So she spent long nights with a torch, red-filtered to prevent

---

* Not literally. No badgers were lofted, lobbed, hefted or used in a
ballistic capacity during the course of this research.

the hedgehogs being scared off by the beam, collecting her participants. Each prickly customer was taken to a mobile lab, where it was gently anaesthetized, weighed, measured and fitted with a radio tag. A selection were also given a tiny injection of 'doubly labelled water', which contains known concentrations of heavy isotopes of oxygen and hydrogen. Afterwards, when each hedgehog was awake and happy,* it was taken back where it had been caught and allowed to return to its usual business.

Once released, unbeknown to the hedgehogs, the clock was ticking. Carly had four days to get detailed tracking information on their movements, and then recapture them to take a tiny blood sample to complete the energetic measurements. The sample would reveal how much of each heavy isotope remained in the hedgehog's body. And that measurement, combined with an understanding of the rates at which the isotopes are metabolized, would allow her to estimate the hedgehogs' energy expenditure, in kilojoules.†

---

* Or at least awake and feeling a bit grumpy and put-upon, but otherwise fine.

† These are the same kJ you get on the back of food packets, which are instantly familiar to anyone who has ever spent any time calorie

At the end of a lot of hard fieldwork, and ferrying hedge-hogs around, Carly had forty-four that had been radio-tracked and for which she had an energy estimate. She had intended to catch equal numbers of hedgehogs in the arable land and the villages, to create a comparison, but only managed to catch two in arable fields. Seventeen were hanging around habitats at the village edge – places like amenity grassland, small pasture fields and set-aside farmland – and the other twenty-five were all in the village, using gardens and road verges. She did still get a comparison, though, because most of the hedgehogs used arable land at some point before the four days ran out – even though they didn't really spend much time there. And the results provided a tantalizing peek into the way hedgehogs juggle their time and energy. First and foremost, hedgehogs that based their activities further from buildings (i.e. further from the core of the village and deeper into the fields) had much larger home ranges. And they used more kilojoules of energy per day, probably because foraging on arable land

---

counting. Or who, like me, gazes at a biscuit tin trying to rationalize down an incontrovertible sugar load. ('You know, it's not too bad. There's a good amount of protein in there, probably from the butter-cream. Anyway, it's fine. Just so long as I don't eat anything else today. Or for most of tomorrow.')

meant doing a lot more work and hiking further to find the invertebrates they needed. Village-foraging hedgehogs, by contrast, could meet all of their nutritional needs within a much smaller area, and limit the amount of running needed. This was found at all of the study sites, regardless of badgers, and suggests that villages might provide better food resources than arable fields. Supplementary food is left by household-ers, but village habitats are also great for invertebrates. Hedgehogs are particularly partial to a juicy worm, and the amenity grasslands around towns and villages can provide these in abundance. In a recent study, earthworm availability was found to be highest in amenity grasslands, followed by woodlands, agricultural grasslands and, last of all (you guessed it), arable land. Arable earthworm populations have suffered badly from modern farming practices, including as a result of soil compaction from heavy modern machinery.

Carly's work also revealed intriguing details concerning how badgers influence hedgehogs' behavioural ecology. With-out badgers, hedgehogs preferred to be in gardens more than right next to buildings. With badgers, this was reversed, with hedgehogs much preferring to stay closer to buildings. Simi-larly, without badgers, 15–25 per cent of hedgehogs' activity took place on arable land, but with badgers this was 0–5 per cent. These findings confirm those from the earlier hedgehog–badger study, but extend them by showing that hedgehogs' range-sizes fell from about 22ha to about 10ha in the presence of badgers. And the daily energy expenditure of the badgered hedgehogs was about a third smaller. This drop in energy use might have been because these hedgehogs were less able or willing to go foraging, preferring to lie low. That behaviour has been shown by a previous study in which hedgehogs foraged less in response to badger odour. It could also be that hedge-hogs compensated for the loss of food intake by conserving energy, by running around less or by going a bit torpid. Regardless of the details, underlying all these explanations is the landscape of fear. Badgers influence hedgehogs' behaviour, with knock-on consequences for food intake and energetic costs.

Overall, villages seem to represent more food, less work and more protection than arable lands. To these observations we can add one more benefit, which is that village habitats are warmer. Hedges are warmer than the centres of fields, yes, but all habitats within villages are warmer than either: 11.9°C on average, compared with 11.4°C for hedges and 10.7°C for field centres. In the words of one hedgehog researcher who has spent a lot of time feeling cold in fields, you can understand why hedgehogs want to be in the villages, because that's where *we* want to be.

Hedgehogs, badgers, farmland, villages. The more we try to separate out these elements and examine them independently, the more they conspire to send us looping back. I have presented more information, but, as in all the best murder mysteries, still we find ourselves with no bloodstained weapon, smoking gun, incriminating note or scrap of exotic cloth to tie our murderer to the crime.* The central problem remains intractable: if badgers, and the fear of badgers, drive hedgehogs from fields and into villages and towns,† the result

---

* I'm reminded of the exchange that reputedly took place between a judge and F. E. Smith, the first Earl of Birkenhead. Judge: I've listened to you for an hour and I'm none the wiser. Smith: None the wiser, perhaps, my lord, but certainly better informed.

† By the way, I use phrases like 'hedgehogs have left farms' or 'hedgehogs have been driven out', but these are shorthand for complex processes that may have occurred over decades. Hedgehogs might well individually disperse in response to experiencing newly abrasive conditions, and rove off to find fortune elsewhere (no doubt incurring a penalty in terms of increased exposure to mortality from badgers and traffic en route). But some hedgehogs may have opted to tough things out, and their populations may have dwindled and died over a number of generations. The end result of all of the processes, however, looks

would look exactly the same as if agricultural intensification had rendered our farmlands inhospitable, and badgers were just one more blameless animal – albeit one with a predilection for hedgehog consumption. We can't prove causation. But neither can we discount either as a cause.

Badgers are implicated. We cannot suggest that badgers are irrelevant, first because the hedgehogs don't act as though they are, and second because at high badger densities hedgehogs stop sharing and start running. But are badgers alone a sufficient explanation? Most likely not, because habitat and invertebrate food availability remain the best predictors of hedgehog presence. Many hedgehogs like to be close to buildings, gardens and amenity grasslands even if badgers aren't around. They often seem to select those habitats regardless.

Agricultural intensification is implicated because, well, how could it not be? Unimaginably vast tracts of prime hedgehog habitat were torn out in one headlong dash for efficiency. We cannot know now how many hedgehogs died as a result, or how large the national population would be if it hadn't happened, but

---

the same – the national population declines, and the hedgehogs' geographical distribution becomes more and more urban.

entire agricultural landscapes have been left devastated. Food and shelter have been stripped away, and hedgehogs that forage on farmlands rather than in villages do so at a demonstrable energetic cost.

The agricultural changes might have been survivable, albeit with drastically reduced hedgehog numbers, if badgers did not exist. And plausibly even the most resurgent of badger populations might have been weathered had the hedges survived the last century intact. But we cannot test these hypotheses. We can only make an educated stab at how our suspects may have colluded in murder. For me, the ecological space for hedgehogs on farms has been wrung out to the last drop. And badgers are administering the final, fatal squeeze. Whatever the proportions of culpability (which I personally would stack heavily on the account of agriculture), the two factors have acted together to render many of our agricultural areas – 75 per cent of the whole UK – and especially the arable fields – 25 per cent of the UK – unliveable for hedgehogs.

This is probably as close as we can get to the truth on current evidence. Carly's fleeing hedgehogs, and those recorded by numerous hedgehog release studies, exemplify in microcosm the fate of hedgehogs up and down rural Britain. Inexorably they are abandoning our fields, pastures and woods, and heading to town to become sophisticated urbanites.

We, along with many countries in northern Europe, have bullied, herded and shoved our hedgehogs a long, long way down the road* towards becoming an exclusively urban species.

A heated discussion is under way in the library of Hotel Furzehoge. The Detective watches, impassive.

'You just don't get it, do you?' Major Geddoff is saying, almost pleading, now. 'It's not intentional. If anything it's the government. If we could make enough money protecting wildlife, we'd do it. But the subsidies are dismal and my chaps get next to nothing for their produce as it is. With the best will in the world, hedgehogs don't pay.'

And that is too much for Ms Nymbies, local parishioner.

'Well, actually, it rather sounds like the poor hedgehogs do pay,' she says. 'Pay with their very lives!' And before Major Geddoff can take breath to reply, she rattles on: 'It's just as well that somebody is prepared to take care of the poor creatures, isn't it? If we can't trust the farming community then the rest of us will just have to step in. The

---

* And then run them over, just for good measure.

local parish will take up the mantle on behalf of our dear, dear hedgehogs.'

The Major subsides, muttering into his whisky. In his place Mr Clarkson leaps up.

'And who says you're not the murderer yourself? I've seen the television programmes and most of these little villages are lethal.' He jabs a finger at Ms Nymbies. 'So before we let Ms Nymbies start "protecting" anybody, maybe we should see a bit of evidence that she's not some murderous mastermind masquerading as a sweet old lady. Am I right?'

The Detective runs an appraising eye over Ms Nymbies' diminutive form. She puts her head on one side.

'Very well. So, Ms Nymbies. What have you got to say to that?'

CHAPTER 5

An Englishman's Home is a Castle (Unfortunately)

I specialize in murders of quiet, domestic
interest.

AGATHA CHRISTIE

A FRINGE BENEFIT OF WILDLIFE RESEARCH IS THAT YOUR friends and colleagues get up to all sorts. I used to share an office with Geraldine, whose research on Himalayan wolves involved a Tibetan field site so remote it took three days' trekking on foot, carrying all her supplies and equipment, just to get to it. My friend Tom sailed in a steel-hulled yacht to the South Sandwich Islands and installed the world's most remote satellite cameras there, to study penguins.* And let's not forget Amy, who once rocked up at a camp in Tanzania, pitched her tent in the wrong place, and spent the night being slept on by

---

* This anecdote is actually a lot more impressive than it sounds. I think it's to do with the islands' name. The South Sandwich Islands sound quite pleasant, like tea and cake might be served on arrival. But to get to them you sail across the world's most deadly ocean, pass the Danger Islands and keep going into truly terrifying seas. When Tom first landed there, more people had set foot on the surface of the moon.

a lion.* These are all worthy contenders, but the inaugural Tom Moorhouse Prize for Weirdly Impressive Commitment to Wildlife Research can only be awarded to Sophie Rasmussen, for going the extra mile under truly bizarre research circumstances. Sophie spent her precious 2020 summer vacation in a Swedish garden, watching a carefully assembled selection of robots slice into the chilly, dead flesh of an array of small hedgehog corpses.† Flawless.

I should probably clear a few things up.‡ Sophie is one of the loveliest people you could hope to meet, and really not the gore and carnage type. She's also famous in Denmark for her love of hedgehogs – in fact, she is known in the Danish media

---

* Few people can claim to have been a lion's mattress. It sauntered into the camp, spotted the one tent that wasn't pitched on a raised wooden platform and thought 'that looks comfy'. Then it hunkered down on top of her for a good snooze. Amy, trapped under felid-flattened canvas, passed out. She was gratified to wake in the morning in possession of all her limbs.

† In her words, it was a massacre. Limbs and organs flew everywhere. Later she walked out on to the grass to find a leg here, and a penis there, and . . . yeah. It was a big mess, something she will never forget.

‡ A narrative job somewhat easier than sanitizing that Swedish lawn when the robots were done.

as 'Dr Hedgehog'.* The flesh-macerating robots were part of a research project into some of the dangers facing hedgehogs in our gardens. They were robot lawnmowers. And, not to sound too apocalyptic, *the robot lawnmowers are coming to a lawn near you.*

Britain has been slow on the uptake. These autonomous grass trimmers are becoming rather popular elsewhere, especially in continental Europe. The global market is predicted to reach US$3.9 billion by 2027. And accompanying the, um, rise of the machines has been a surge in reports of injured hedgehogs. So Sophie decided to investigate.

Some research projects are relatively simple to set up. This was one of the other ones. Sophie ended up testing eighteen different types of lawnmower, each equipped with different collision detection systems, ultrasonic sensors and variously slashy, tumbly or whirly blade arrangements. The idea was to see what happened if they encountered juvenile and adult hedgehogs, in enough different relative positions and orientations to do a proper assessment. Sophie lived in Denmark and managed to get permission to use seventy dead hedgehogs,

---

* The Danish for hedgehog is 'pindsvin', which literally translates as 'stick-pig'. Fun challenge: work that fact into a passing conversation.

deep-frozen and sourced from various Danish carers she knows. But the tests took place in Sweden. Which meant transporting seventy dead hedgehogs across international borders during a pandemic. None of the relevant authorities had ever expected to have to issue a permit for this, and so didn't know how. (In fact, the employee who answered the first call thought it was a prank, and hung up.) But after some negotiation a car full of hedgehog cadavers in cooler bags, driven by a slightly hysterical hedgehog researcher with two assistants, eventually pulled up at a private garden, at an undisclosed location in rural Sweden. There Sophie set to work with the technicians arranging defrosted hedgehogs in front of robotic lawnmowers. The technicians weren't necessarily as hedgehog-obsessed as she was, but they were nice people, many were vegetarians, and everyone was on the hedgehogs' side. Everyone wanted the lawnmowers to detect the hedgehogs, stop, change course and leave the hedgehogs unmolested to scamper away.*

What actually happened ran the full gamut between 'small nudge with a direction change' and 'keep right on mowing, regardless of the smell'. Nearly all of the dependent-

---

* Not these specific hedgehogs, you understand. That would have raised questions.

juvenile-sized hedgehog corpses got mown over. Which is bad, but there is perhaps an argument that had their mothers been present the collision might somehow have been avoided. With respect to the adults, damage varied with various lawnmower designs. Sophie assigned different categories to collisions based on damage to the cadavers. The two of interest are Category 3 and Category 4. Category 3 meant the lawnmower drove across the hedgehog, causing the machine to be lifted and the blades to stop running. When this happened injuries ranged from 'undetectable' to 'the cutting of a small number of spines, but might have involved minor bruising to a live hedgehog'.* Category 4 involved nasty wounds, lethal if left untreated. If we take that latter category as our benchmark, seven of the eighteen models passed all ten trials (i.e. they did not inflict any wounds). All the other eleven models would have killed at least one hedgehog, and some would have killed most of them. If we take a more stringent benchmark of not causing any injury in Category 3 or above, only one model passed all ten tests.

There are arguments surrounding whether live hedgehogs could run away (they could) or *would* run away (debatable – and

---

* And probably a full-on heart attack and/or a lifetime of PTSD.

if they curled up the outcome could be grisly) from the mowers. But the good news is that the industry, to its credit, engaged to the extent necessary to get this testing done. And so we have data showing the existence of a potential novel threat to hedgehogs from certain models of robotic lawnmower, and data on which models are less likely to be a problem. If you were thinking of buying a robot lawnmower, and feel that your lawn might be more attractive if not strewn with gaily decorative hedgehog willies, you may wish to have a quick read about Sophie's research on the subject.*

Hedgehogs really don't need anything else making their lives dangerous. Especially not in our gardens. Robotic lawn-mowers are clearly not the end-all of hedgehog conservation, but they are a straw added to the burden of an already dod-dery dromedary. You don't need to speak to many hedgehog carers to hear a laundry list of the nasty accidents that can befall urban hedgehogs, almost all with human negligence as their cause. Strimmers are the more common equivalent of

---

* It's open to anyone: https://www.mdpi.com/2076-2615/11/5/1191/ html. See table 4 therein if you don't want to read the whole thing. She also has a YouTube video channel called 'Dr Hedgehog' where she explains the results.

the robotic lawnmowers, and careless use can inflict life-ending injuries. More than one researcher has radio-tracked hedgehogs that later were found to have been strimmed. Many receive a close shave, leaving bald patches of spines, but worse strimming can and does occur. Beyond grass cutting, you can find electric fencing in many rural villages that have horses, small livestock or poultry. If well maintained, it has a gap between the base and the ground, to prevent the current going into the grass. If badly maintained, with electrified strands at ground level, it can kill hedgehogs. Most of us would get a jolt and leap away. A hedgehog curls up and keeps getting shocked until it dies. This is especially an issue for mesh fences (like those used for chickens) which are even easier to get tangled up in.

Mesh in general isn't great for hedgehogs, especially garden netting and cricket/tennis nets. People do often eventually find, and disentangle, any caught hedgehogs, but sometimes not quickly enough. And we all know – don't we? – about minimizing the use of slug pellets (or buying hedgehog-friendly slug pellets),* checking bonfires for nesting hogs before setting

---

* There is oddly scant evidence regarding the effects of slug pellets. The lethal dose of metaldehyde, the active ingredient, is extremely high for

light to them, and ensuring that our garden ponds and water features have escape routes that can be navigated by something with short legs that finds it hard to clamber over things. (A few bricks in the water, or a little ramp of wood or wire mesh, will do the job.) Then there are cats and dogs and urban foxes to contend with, all of which can make life fatally unpleasant for hedgehogs. And, of course, urban areas come as part of a package deal that involves roads and cars and all their inherent dangers. Finally, there are all the tiny, seemingly inconsequential, but lethal things we do. Discarded rubber bands from Royal Mail packages, for example, have recently been highlighted as causing some horrible hedgehog injuries and fatalities – they get stuck around the body or on a limb,

---

hedgehogs, requiring them to eat about five thousand poisoned slugs before it would kill them. But nobody really knows whether there are sub-lethal effects on hedgehogs' breeding or immunity or general health. And there is also convincing work that suggests that hedgehogs might *directly* consume slug pellets, in which case as little as 5g could be lethal. So as with all these cases – which relate equally to every agricultural chemical ever applied – we absolutely should, but never do, apply the precautionary principle and avoid usage wherever possible. For more on this, see Pat Morris, *Hedgehogs* (Whittet Books, 1983); Nigel Reeve, *Hedgehogs*, Poyser Natural History series (Poyser, 1994), p. 247.

and slowly constrict and embed as the hedgehog grows. Not a good way to go, and eminently avoidable.

There are also less obvious negatives associated with urban areas. A study of twenty-two hedgehogs in Berlin, over four years, compared the intensity of artificial light in areas where the hedgehogs were active, versus the background average of light intensity. It showed that the hedgehogs were seeking out and preferentially spending their time in areas where the intensity of artificial light was lowest. We don't know why. Perhaps they didn't like the light. Or perhaps the hedgehogs' food was avoiding the lights, and so that's where the hedgehogs went. Or perhaps they wanted to avoid humans, human concrete structures and traffic, and because all these human-associated things tend to be accompanied by bright lights, the hedgehogs end up in the darker, quieter areas by default. It could be any or all of these explanations, but urban hedgehogs certainly don't like too much human disturbance. When a two-day music festival arrived in a hedgehog-inhabited park in Berlin (with days of construction and dismantling either side), hedgehogs there decreased their range sizes, moved more slowly, rested less, searched around more intensely and moved away from the centre of their previous ranges. They curled up more frequently and stayed in the bushes where they nested or at the edges of the park, rather than heading to their usual foraging grounds. All of which is to say that they struggled to deal with a horrible new source of stress in their lives.

The same study showed that, when confronted with a habitat full of barriers that can't be slipped through, hedgehogs compensate behaviourally, increasing the size of their home ranges and the speed at which they move around. In this case it was brick barriers and concrete paths in a small zoological park that had the effect of turning the hedgehogs' home into a mosaic of suitable patches. The unsuitable habitats have to be traversed or navigated around. Ecologists call these 'matrix' habitats. Habitat fragmentation occurs when the landscape becomes a mosaic of matrix and suitable habitats, forcing animals to adjust how they move. Put simply, fragmentation makes it more difficult to find food and mates. The greater the fragmentation, the more one big population gets split into lots of little independent ones, each of which is just a bit more vulnerable than it used to be. In towns and cities, the ratio of matrix to green space tends to get higher as you head towards the centre. At some point the effort required to navigate it all, and the risks involved, become too large, and you will stop finding hedgehogs. The matrix-to-green-space ratio has probably also altered over time, as we have progressively infilled and extended, constructed roads and shopping centres, and repurposed our towns and boroughs to accommodate more humans, more comfortably. Every new convenience is purpose-built to exclude wildlife.

There are clear drawbacks for hedgehogs to choosing urban habitats. The increasing prevalence of unfortunate incidents occurring in agricultural landscapes* is echoed by the ever-more-ingenious ways in which humans make our own lives more comfortable, while making life more dangerous, difficult and disconcerting for hedgehogs. But then, for a small mammal *everywhere* is perilous, difficult and disconcerting. What is important to understand is whether or not the price of being urban is worth paying. To put this another way, some of the hedgehog mortality, and some of the required behavioural adjustments, could be amply compensated for by the removal of other sources of mortality, and by the improved food and shelter on offer. If, overall, the benefits yielded a breeding rate higher than the mortality rate, urban hedgehogs would thrive. The important question, then, is whether that's the case, and

---

* The most unfortunate hedgehog I heard about was a radio-tracked juvenile who had taken to foraging in a large, grassy field full of cows. He was found dead in the centre of the field. The cause of death was easy to establish. The hedgehog was face down in a flattened 'V' shape, having been drilled bodily down into the turf by a cow's hoof. Nasty.

if so whether it is reflected in urban hedgehog numbers. Are those numbers booming, stable or (gulp) declining?

We don't fully know, but two national surveys provide an indication. The People's Trust for Endangered Species' Living with Mammals survey and the British Trust for Ornithology's Garden BirdWatch both ask volunteers to submit records of hedgehogs in urban areas (most often gardens). The Living with Mammals survey began in 2003, and has been running ever since. It indicates that between 2003 and 2013 there was a 25 per cent decline in the proportion of urban sites at which hedgehogs were found – only about three-quarters of sites with hedgehogs in 2003 still had them in 2013 – but that the occupied proportion has since held stable at that three-quarters mark. The Garden BirdWatch survey tells a similar but subtly different story. The hedgehog trend between the first year (2009) and 2013 shows a similar initial decline in hedgehog occupancy, after which the proportion of occupied locations increases up to around 110 per cent of what it had been at the outset in 2009 (suggesting that hedgehog occupancy has now increased overall).

Of the two surveys we should probably assume the Living with Mammals is more accurate. The Garden BirdWatch survey is primarily for people interested in birds, and recording mammals is optional. That means that we cannot be certain that places that didn't record hedgehogs were looking for them in the first place. The solution adopted was to limit analyses to just those participants who recorded at least one mammal (and who we therefore know were looking for mammals), ensuring that any hedgehog absences were true absences. But the downside of that is it excludes participants who *were* recording mammals, but didn't see any. And so it runs the risk of removing some true hedgehog absences, and thereby overestimating numbers. So on balance it seems most likely that the trend identified was a mild overestimate, and there has been a 25 per cent decline in the proportion of hedgehog-inhabited urban locations, but that at least it hasn't got worse since 2013.

Both of these surveys also allow participants to record hedgehog numbers to create a maximum weekly abundance of hedgehogs at a given site. They agree that there was an initial decline that then reversed around 2013, and that weekly abundance is now slightly higher than in the first year of both surveys. Before we begin the celebratory dancing,* however,

---

* I'll leave the choice of dance to you, but I can recommend my toddler's personal favourite of 'around the kitchen in my pants'. (Her pants. Not my pants.)

we need to bear in mind that these would be higher densities of hedgehogs across a smaller number of sites. And even those higher densities are open to question, because people are increasingly using cheaply available technology like trail cameras to record hedgehogs, which makes counting individuals a lot easier. It could well be that hedgehog abundance hasn't changed, but people's ability not to miss individuals has improved. Taking the evidence all together, the closest we can get to a conclusion is that numbers in urban areas are largely holding steady after decreasing earlier this century.

What neither of these surveys can do is enable us to compare the current status of urban hedgehogs with their status at any point in the twentieth century. We don't know whether the 2003 baseline is a miserly fraction of some humongous number of 1970s urban hedgehogs. It is, sadly, a fair bet that something like that is the case. We have what Hugh Warwick terms 'anecdata', derived from lots of people now drawing pensions who all recall hedgehogs being a lot more visible around their properties than they are now. But we can't rely a lot on those remembrances. Some of the little hard evidence there is on this comes not from Britain, but from Switzerland. A recent study compared data collected through citizen-science projects conducted in Zurich in 1992 and 2016–18. It concluded that hedgehogs had lost 18 per cent of their former distribution, and declined in abundance from 32 per square kilometre to 19 per square kilometre. The authors examined a lot of potential causes, but found nothing conclusive. And whether similar trends have occurred elsewhere, including Britain, is, of course, unknown – this study was the first ever to quantify the decline rate of urban hedgehogs in any European city over a long period of time.

The recent British data are not disastrous, but they aren't brilliant either – losing about a quarter of some of the last remaining hedgehog populations in ten years looks pretty dicey. If our parks and gardens are to act as a lifeline for a species, we need them to perform that function a lot better than they do. Unlike aspects of British conservation that occur in national parks or in farmlands, over which we individually have little say or input, urban hedgehogs are very clearly in our bailiwick. The actions we take in our own homes and in our shared spaces can have direct effects on hedgehogs and their survival. And clearly, collectively, we need to make improvements.

The question, though, is what? *What* should we be improving? Are robot lawnmowers, cars and bonfires the problem, or are the larger forces of urban fragmentation and habitat loss making our villages, towns and cities deficient? And how can we tell?

One way to start addressing this question is to reverse it. Rather than asking what might be going wrong, we can ask what a stable population of hedgehogs in a town looks like, and what sort of space they would need to occupy. That could allow us to derive a rough blueprint of the minimum we should be doing to preserve the species in a given location. And then we can set about seeing whether we are likely to meet that minimum in most of our towns. First, what we need is an estimate of the minimum viable population size (or 'MVP') of hedgehogs – the number below which a local population is doomed to disappear. The MVP intuitively has to be more than a couple of hedgehogs in a garden, because one fox or strimmer* in the wrong place could permanently end that population, as could overusing the slug pellets, or a couple of cold winters. And also, intuitively, some immense collection of interconnected gardens hosting a thousand hedgehogs should be almost certain to still be occupied a hundred years from now. (Because even many consecutive bad years, in which death rates exceeded birth rates, wouldn't drive such a big

---

* Or a fox *with* a strimmer. They're intelligent, it's only a matter of time.

population to zero, and the hedgehogs could bounce back when things improved.) But we're unlikely to be able to achieve enough space for a thousand hedgehogs in people's gardens. So we need to calculate a realistic figure that lies somewhere between the two extremes.

Working out an MVP for hedgehogs is what I spent a chunk of 2013 doing, commissioned by the People's Trust for Endangered Species. To do it, I used some ominously named software called 'VORTEX'.* VORTEX is information-hungry. You feed it things like how many litters of how many babies a female can have, how many in a litter on average, how variable this is, what percentage of females breed in a given year, how likely a litter is to survive, how likely an adult is to survive, how long the species lives on average, how long an individual lives, how old they are when they first breed, how big the starting

---

* It's named after an ecological concept called an 'extinction vortex', which occurs when a population's death rate consistently exceeds the birth rate. With every generation the population gets smaller until it disappears, like it's circling a plughole. The circumstances could, for example, occur if the population's habitat has been reduced in size, food gets scarce, the climate changes, or a new disease or predator moves in. It's quite a melancholy concept because at any given time point the population exists, but it's nevertheless on a path to disappearance.

population should be, and a whole host of other detailed ecological stuff – and it takes these data and creates thousands of simulated populations. From these, it calculates the likelihood of a population of a given size still existing, say, a hundred years from now.

After months of pulling hedgehog ecological and life-history data out of the academic literature,* and stuffing it into computer simulations, I found myself in possession of two best-guess MVPs – one for rural hedgehogs and one for urban hedgehogs. The simulations suggested that in areas with less food and shelter, and more predation (i.e. rural populations), you would probably need about 120–250 hedgehogs to guarantee population survival for a hundred years. By contrast, urban hedgehogs could get by with 32–60 individuals. The key differences came from the higher mortality rates in the countryside and the amount of inter-annual variation in

---

* And hair out of my head at all of the variously contradictory and later-proven-to-be-inaccurate values contained therein. Variations in study locations and methodology meant that everything needed scrutinizing, justifying, comparing to results of later studies and then wrangling into a format that the software could use. By the end of the study I had a headache from all the scowling, and a deep suspicion that somebody, somewhere, was taking the mick.

food availability. In rural areas, hedgehog food will be a matter of boom or bust, depending on the weather. A bad invertebrate year means a bad breeding and survival year. In urban areas, the food is more consistently available, partly because it is often provided by humans, and this makes a heck of a difference to the stability of hedgehog numbers.

Thirty or so hedgehogs appears to be the absolute minimum population size that could be expected to survive, even under the very best of conditions. But it would probably be sensible to take the value as being closer to fifty or sixty. Combine these numbers with recorded hedgehog densities in different habitats and you can calculate a rough estimate of the minimum amount of habitat a hedgehog population needs. In rural areas, this comes in at between 4 and 57km^2, probably closer to the latter. Space needed in urban areas is far less, about 1 to 2.5 km^2.* So once again, urban habitats have a demonstrable advantage, because they can be a lot smaller and still host a viable hedgehog population. And this is great news, because your average village, town or city has masses of green spaces

---

* The exception is inner-city areas, which tend to contain a lot less good hedgehog habitat, meaning you'd need about 8km^2 of inner city to do the job of a decent 2km^2 of suburban parks and gardens.

and gardens that can handily combine to support hedgehogs. A quarter of the area of a typical city is gardens (which comprise about half a city's green space). There are something like 22.7 million gardens in the UK, with a total area of 4,330 km². A back-of-the-envelope calculation suggests that even if we ignore playing fields and parks, the UK's gardens alone could support something like 39,000–139,000 hedgehogs, or a good two to four thousand stable hedgehog populations.

So our gardens sound like they could form an okay backstop position. Even if hedgehogs were eradicated from the countryside, they could exist in our towns. But there's a twist in this conclusion. Because hedgehog habitat is only any use if hedgehogs can actually get at it. And for many homeowners the answer to the question 'Exactly how accessible is your garden to hedgehogs?' is likely to be: 'Um, no idea. Look, I've just put a new fence in, is there a problem?'

Ms Nymbies is appalled. Having given a full account of her good standing within the parish and scornfully refuted any suggestion that she or her gardener might have accidentally strimmed any hedgehogs to death, she is now busying herself with mentally composing letters to her local MP and several county councillors. She frowns when the Detective interrupts her train of thought.

'Ms Nymbies, I have a question. Have you seen any hedgehogs yourself, recently? In your own garden, perhaps?'

Ms Nymbies hesitates. 'Well, not really, no. Not now I think of it.' She hesitates, then continues in a strident voice. 'And that's a crying shame. If ever one came to my house I'm quite sure I would provide a warm welcome and scrummy delicious food. Yes, they really should visit, shouldn't they? It's such a lovely safe garden too.'

'Is that a fact?' says the Detective.

'Oh yes, we had it secured. Great big walls all round. Can't imagine why the silly things don't come to visit.'

'Right.' The Detective runs a hand over her eyes. 'I believe I may have solved the mystery of your personal lack of hedgehogs, Ms Nymbies.' She raises her voice to be heard over the growing hubbub. 'And moreover I believe that I am close to solving our wider puzzle. Ladies and gentlemen, just a few final pieces remain . . .'

I live in a classic back-to-back terrace in east Oxford. The houses form four sides of a rough rectangle, surrounding the gardens within. Each garden has two side fences separating it from its neighbours, and a rear fence separating it from the garden opposite. My postage-stamp-sized offering of lawn, flowerbed and shed lies bang in the middle of this lot and hasn't been visited by a hedgehog at any point in the decade since I moved in. This is not surprising. The houses are jammed up against one another with no side entrances, and so there is no real way into the rectangle of gardens except at the corners. Even then, for a hedgehog to get to those corners means crossing roads and navigating pavements en route from another patch of presumably less-than-accessible gardens. I've seen precisely one hedgehog on our street and . . . well, let's just say it was geometrically challenged, following an altercation with a truck. Add to this unpromising situation a recent flurry of pandemic home improvements, in the form of rickety fences being replaced with thick timber-down-to-the-ground jobs, and we are left with a few hectares of prime hedgehog habitat that have inadvertently been rendered utterly useless for the species.

But you can find hedgehogs in a near-identical terrace in the centre of Ipswich. They are there in quite high densities, in a place where researchers were convinced there was no point looking: terraced housing, very urbanized, very little green space, no front gardens, no side access. What makes the difference is that in the Ipswich terrace a narrow path runs between the two rows of back gardens, and the hedgehogs can use it to gain access. In my patch of Oxford a path probably existed in the days of outside toilets, but is now long gone.

And while various of my neighbours' fences are in a laudable state of disrepair, full of holes a hedgehog could use, far too many are being maintained to a nicety of hedgehog exclusion.

It really needn't be this way. It is very simple to put a single hole, about the size of a CD case, into a fence panel. And preferably to do that on three sides. And then any hedgehogs around can scamper happily into previously inaccessible spaces and make use of the habitats therein. A recent modelling exercise, based on hedgehogs in the German city of Braunschweig, suggested that if every garden and allotment were closed off, this would reduce the amount of key habitat available to hedgehogs by 63 per cent, compared with a situation in which all were available. The most important component were the gardens, comprising 50 per cent, with allotments making up the other 13 per cent. Similarly, the amount of resistance hedgehogs would experience moving around the urban landscape would be 73 per cent lower if all gardens were accessible. So hedgehogs should really benefit from any attempt to improve entry to our gardens.

Nobody has tested the theory in practice. Which is not to say they haven't tried. But if you thought, on the basis of my previous

descriptions,* that studying wildlife in the countryside is difficult, you should try working on an urban species. Although
warmer and more convenient, urban fieldwork has the major
drawback of requiring researchers to engage repeatedly with the
most tricky component of any ecological research project: people.
Getting permission to traipse across someone's property is hard.
In the countryside you can target a few landowners and after
some begging get access to a lot of habitat. In towns and cities,
you are forever asking permission to go poking and prying
around people's gardens, often at night.† And while many homeowners are amazingly accommodating, getting hard data on
hedgehogs in urban areas has proved extraordinarily tricky.

---

* Or whingings, call them what you will.

† When I was an undergraduate, one of my lecturers told a possibly
apocryphal tale about surveying urban slug populations. The survey
required a researcher literally to crawl down a path on hands and
knees, at night, Dictaphone in hand, naming species of slugs as they
were spotted. It was going fine until he encountered a large pair of
boots. These were attached to a police officer. The officer was eager to
understand exactly what the researcher thought they were doing,
crawling down an alley behind a row of high-street banks. The
explanation of 'I'm recording slug species on this Dictaphone' was
received with some scepticism, and resulted in a night in the cells.

No project exemplifies the difficulty of studying hedgehogs in towns better than the work of Abi Gazzard and Phil Baker at Reading University.* They had a really great idea. Putting 'hedgehog highways'† into fences is being promoted by Hedgehog Street – a joint initiative by the People's Trust for Endangered Species and British Hedgehog Preservation Society – as a conservation measure. The Reading team's idea was to test whether hedgehog highways actually deliver demonstrable benefits in terms of hedgehogs' abilities to access a

---

* Well, there is another wonderful example, and it's from Sophie again. A hedgehog she was tracking in a Danish city slipped into a playground belonging to a nursery. The playground was enclosed by a 3m high chain-link fence intertwined with a dense beech hedge. And, inside, the hedgehog was groaning in apparent agony, like it was choking or suffering from a horrible chest infection. Sophie found a bench, dragged it up to the fence, and clambered over. Inside she found the hedgehog in the throes of a romantic engagement with a rather lovely female. It was not at all grateful to be interrupted. The hedgehogs ran off, leaving Sophie locked in a nursery at night with no way out and no evidence to corroborate her explanation. Her escape involved a call to her mother-in-law, uprooting a massive iron bench, and a call to the nursery to apologize the next morning. They were, apparently, very understanding.

† Aka 'holes'.

variety of gardens during a night's bimbling about. The project design was deceptively simple: identify homeowners who are willing to get involved, and then track hedgehogs around their properties to see how they are moving. Next step, get the homeowners to put a couple of holes in their fences, and see what sort of a difference this makes to the places the hedgehogs go. What could possibly go wrong?

Just to make sure the experiment would work, Abi first tried a pilot. She knocked on doors in Reading and asked folks to fill in surveys about their gardens, including whether they would be willing, in theory, to create a hedgehog highway. She got good responses from about six hundred people, and of those, something like 80 per cent said they would be willing to put in a highway. These were, of course, very encouraging results. So next the team identified a nearby area for the actual experiment. They contacted five hundred more households asking if they would want to get involved and install some holes for hedgehogs. And faced with the prospect of actually doing something, almost nobody signed up.

In response, the Reading team employed a time-honoured research-study fallback panacea for community engagement, known as 'bribery'. Working with the PTES, they created a lottery with a £1,000 top prize, and some wildlife cameras for any household willing to cut hedgehog highways. But even with cash to be won, and a huge time input from Abi, on the practical matter of making a few holes in fences people stayed resolutely unengaged. Only two holes got cut. And of the on-paper-enthusiastic houses in the original pilot study, only one person actually made a highway – which was later blocked up by their neighbour, who said he'd 'seen rats' using it.*

Academics are hard people to deter. The team figured that the difficulty in Reading might have been socio-economic, or might have come about because the researchers were outsiders, essentially asking for a favour. So they tried again, this time in a relatively affluent part of Oxford. They created a community group called 'Hinksey Hogs' and set up a small team of volunteers led by a really enthusiastic local volunteer. They also drafted in Hugh Warwick, who lives in Oxford, to help persuade folks to take part. They did the whole thing again, with lots of footprint tunnel surveys, nocturnal surveys, stalls and lectures to get people interested. And Hugh, who is

---

* Blocking up a hedgehog hole is never going to prevent rats – burrowing animals that by the time you've seen them will already have an extensive network of sub-fence tunnels – from frolicking on your property. But it may well, of course, severely inconvenience a hedgehog.

enthusiasm incarnate, gave a wonderful motivating talk. And this time about three people made holes.

So a good, simple idea failed in practice. And the project changed tack to examine *why* it had failed. Because on the face of it, it shouldn't have. As Phil Baker says, he used to work on urban foxes and pet cats, two animals that really divide opinions, and thought that hedgehogs would be a breeze, given that everybody loves them. But apparently not everyone loves hedgehogs even enough to cut a small hole into or under their fence.

In addition to asking people face to face what had held them back from making the highways, the researchers constructed online surveys to ask a variety of questions, including why they wouldn't cut holes. They surveyed the general public but also Hedgehog Champions, the brilliant souls who have signed up to the Hedgehog Street campaign. And the results were pretty clear. People who had made highways were twice as likely to have heard of Hedgehog Street, and were already massively engaged with the environment, and had installed loads of wildlife-friendly features in their gardens. Hedgehog Champions on average were responsible for creating about 1.69 highways each, divided between their own gardens and those of other people they had persuaded.

Extrapolating these figures to the total number of Hedgehog Champions (over seventy thousand of them) would equate to the creation of more than 120,000 highways connecting more than 240,000 gardens, equivalent to approximately 1.1 per cent of UK households with access to a garden. Not bad.

But the average highway-installation rate belies something of a bifurcation among the Hedgehog Champions. Only just under half of them managed to get any highways cut at all. Those who did created 3.5 highways each, on average. The other half created none. Among non-Champions, the rate of highway installation was low: of people who had *not* come across Hedgehog Street, only 6–30 per cent said they had installed a highway. And the worse news is that these people weren't necessarily representative of the wider public, because respondents self-selected to participate in the survey. The folks who filled out and returned the forms tended to be people already engaged in wildlife-friendly activities. They were far more likely to have fed birds (81 per cent said they had), created a pond (40 per cent) and/or put up a bird box (68 per cent), compared to the national average (51 per cent, 16 per cent and 21 per cent, respectively).

By far the most common reason given for not having a highway was that the garden was already accessible to hedgehogs. The next most common was that they didn't want to talk to their neighbours or put a strain on that relationship by 'being difficult'. Unlike putting up a bird box, planting some wild flowers or engaging with 'no-mow May', all of which you would feel perfectly entitled to do on your own property, cutting a hole in a fence without engaging in considerable upfront diplomacy feels like inciting the British-neighbourly equivalent of the Cold War.* And that's assuming you actually own your house. If you are merely renting, then there is probably no way that fence is getting touched. The next most common reason for hole avoidance was that people assumed there were no hedgehogs where they lived, and so didn't see any point in making a hole for them. The eagle-eyed may spot a logical flaw in this latter explanation. Because just maybe the reason you haven't seen a hedgehog in the neighbourhood is that *they can't get into any gardens because there are no holes.*† But

---

* 'Did you *see* what they did to our shared boundary? I'll give them such a tutting-at, they'll be reeling, *reeling*, I tell you.'

† Also bear in mind that in general people are awful at knowing if there are hedgehogs in their gardens. Time and again Abi found herself speaking to homeowners who'd say 'Oh, I've never seen a hedgehog here', while she knew that she had radio-tracked a hedgehog through there pretty recently. Hedgehogs are nocturnal, and so tend to be out

there is also a less obvious logical flaw with the first reason, which is that the presence of hedgehogs does not render additional holes pointless. The holes are important not only as a single entryway, used to get in and out of just one property, but also as a way to connect into other people's gardens, and onward.

Is people's unwillingness to cut holes for hedgehogs a problem? Well, because the study didn't work, we can't be sure. A lot of hedgehog permeability hinges on housing type (terraced vs semis vs detached) and fence maintenance, which probably also reflects people's affluence and when the houses were built. A lot of newbuilds are notably hedgehog-proof, with gravel boards under fences that effectively block access to gardens and potentially also entire swathes of habitat beyond them. Again, here, hedgehog highways would be a lifeline. But beyond those, hedgehogs can and do squeeze through some pretty small gaps. Phil Baker used to live in a 1980s house, which had a small garden containing a shed and a

---

when we're not. Most people are completely unaware of the wildlife shenanigans that occur in their gardens in the small hours. I've had everything from foxes (which sometimes dig under the fences, and sometimes run across the shed roofs to gain entry) to sparrowhawks in my own garden, and I live in the middle of Oxford.

trampoline and virtually no shrubs. He assumed he'd never get hedgehogs, until he was woken at 3 a.m. by the sound of two of them getting frisky. He put out a bowl of food the next night and got *three* hedgehogs in the garden. They had squeezed through a gap 12cm wide and 4–5cm deep under his fence for the purposes of using his garden as a boudoir. Similarly, hedgehogs have been recorded happily trotting down the side of a house, under the gate, along the pavement and back through a side gate into the next garden. There's an obvious, if slight, cost to having to follow that longer path, in terms of time spent and energy expended, but they do it. The counter-argument to both of these anecdotes, of course, is that the hedgehogs would undoubtedly prefer life to be a lot easier, and a couple of small holes in fences would achieve that in no time.

There are likely to be benefits for hedgehogs of a highway or two even if you already get prickly night-time visitors,* but especially if you don't. The benefits might be marginal, some-times, but in other cases could be substantial. And, of course, the precautionary principle dictates that engaging in one small, potentially vital action, even if the benefit is unproven,

---

* For clarity, I mean hedgehogs.

is probably better than the worst case of watching urban hedgehog populations disappear. And in any case, aside from requiring the horribly cringeworthy act of striking up a conversation with your neighbours, it's not really a big job. So that is one easy step we can all take. And there is definitely more you can do to make your garden attractive. Abi and Phil's work didn't get many holes made, but it did provide a lovely dataset of features of people's gardens that they could compare with how much time their radio-tagged hedgehogs spent there.

If you want to know what else you can do to attract hedgehogs into your garden, the single most simple advice is to give them food. A lot of people feed hedgehogs, and now you can even buy speciality hedgehog food in supermarkets. If the food supply is predictable and regular, the hedgehogs will be coming back and back. As ever, Pat Morris got there first. His early studies demonstrated that hedgehogs are able to remember a nice feed station and incorporate that into their nightly routine, sometimes making a beeline for it, but sometimes taking in a few other sights en route. Pat concluded that the hedgehogs basically treat the food as they would any other decent feeding patch. It's something to be included in the rounds, but not necessarily worth making a detour for. But there are some signs that supplementary food these days could play a rather more significant role in a hedgehog's life.* Abi's work has shown than in the autumn (when hedgehogs are preparing for hibernation), hedgehogs are found in 84 per cent of gardens where they have been fed, versus 34 per cent where they have not. And in winter there was an even bigger difference – 64 per cent of gardens versus just 8 per cent of gardens. Similarly, hedgehogs spend a disproportionate amount of their time in people's gardens, relative to other urban habitats, but especially opt for gardens where people are feeding hedgehogs, and/or where there is a compost heap. Compost heaps, of course, are a great source of both nesting materials and invertebrate prey. Finally, observations from Sophie Rasmussen's work on Danish hedgehogs agree with Abi's findings from Reading. Sophie found that her radio-tracked urban hedgehogs tended to stay in the vicinity of local feeding

---

* This is speculation, though. In 1985 Pat's feeding stations tended to offer bread and milk, whereas these days the food left out tends to be cat food or special hedgehog food. I can easily imagine hedgehogs making a special detour for a high-protein diet, but not being too bothered by the bread-and-milk option. I can equally easily imagine that natural food in our gardens is getting scarce and supplementary food is therefore taking on more importance. But without data, who knows?

stations, mainly using gardens that surrounded the one offering food.

Hedgehogs attach a lot of importance to the food we leave them. That food in turn will affect some pretty fundamental bits of their ecology. In the breeding season it should help increase litter sizes and the survival prospects of both juveniles and adults, and therefore should boost population densities. And in the winter it appears to increase the likelihood of hedgehogs staying active when they might otherwise be expected to hibernate. In the latter case we don't know enough to say whether this is a benefit or a detriment to the hedgehogs. It could be that the food is insufficient to compensate for the costs of moving around in freezing weather, and so might push hedgehogs into an energetic deficit. Or alternatively, supplementary food might offer life support to hedgehogs that otherwise wouldn't make it through the winter. We simply don't know. So in terms of guidance, it sounds like feeding through the spring, summer and autumn are likely to be good things, and if you do feed in winter it may be a good thing so long as you keep going and don't suddenly stop one day.

Again, there are many unanswered questions. Are modern, urban hedgehogs reliant on supplementary feeding? If you put down high-quality food it seems you become *the* restaurant in the area, but is this because the hedgehogs are intelligent, only going where the food is good, or does it indicate that natural food has started to get scarce in urban habitats, so when something rich pops up they all head there as a matter of necessity? We don't know. It's yet one more uncertainty added to a very long list.

Urban hedgehogs are some of the wild animals that come closest to us of any, a species that would happily trot into our own gardens on a nightly basis if they could only get in. We should know all about them, but crucial questions remain. We are left in the invidious position of being unable to be sure that the species can survive alongside us. For now, they seem to be doing okay, if not as well as they could. But the risk is that change is afoot and we are sleepwalking into trouble. Urban areas may well represent a stronghold, but what does that mean? The stronghold might only be strong in comparison with what's happening in rural areas. Could it be that hedgehogs are declining everywhere, but it's just happening at a slower rate in our towns and cities?

We cannot, surely, take a chance on assuming that urban populations are robust, or that they will stay that way. Not without evidence. Not given how important they have become.

We must assume that they are fragile, and do everything we can to ensure that what hedgehog populations we have left are as good as they possibly can be. But the guess of many hedgehog researchers is that we're collectively headed the other way. Much of urban ecology is the study of how tiny changes accumulate over time to yield substantial impacts on urban species. Phil Baker recalls that in 2007 there was an ornamental garden on the University of Reading campus, and the first time he visited it he found ten hedgehogs in two hours. But as money in universities became tighter the management of the grounds was altered, to cut costs. They snipped a few hedgerows, put bark-chips down and mowed everything a bit more frequently. And in response to these modest changes, the hedgehogs became elusive. You can go there now, and not see one.

Gardens are vital hedgehog habitats, but the insidious forces of tidiness and convenience continue to creep in, devaluing them by the day. A fence here, a patio there, an overly cropped lawn, slug pellets, a shed on a concrete base, some decking, perhaps a patch of artificial turf: all to create a nice, neat space in which you can sit with a beer, or host a barbecue. Reasonable modifications of these sorts can be found in gardens everywhere. And while robot lawnmowers might sound like a ridiculous extravagance, something that nobody really needs, you still wouldn't bet against them being adopted. Because they save that little bit of time and effort – at the cost, perhaps, of a few more unseen wildlife casualties.

We treat our gardens as accessories to our lives. They must fit around the clamour of our obligations and chronic busyness. It's nice to have an orderly space in which we can settle back, shut things out and relax for a bit. But when we think in those terms we forget that our gardens are a home for many other species as well. We forget that gardens are not a possession, but a shared resource. We are changing, in small increments, habitats on which other animals rely for survival. Each step towards neatness is small of itself, a paper cut, an inconvenience, something negligible.

But we have all heard of death by a thousand cuts.

CHAPTER 6

A Murderer Unmasked

We are all complicit, and farmer-bashing is
not going to help . . . if farmers were to
vanish, most of us would be dead within a
year.

DAVE GOULSON
The Garden Jungle

Anyone . . . who is able to advance even a
little ought to be of good cheer . . .

PLATO,
The Sophist (trans. Benjamin Jowett)

THE LIBRARY OF HOTEL FURZEHOGE HAS NEVER BEEN THIS silent. It has been quieter and emptier, certainly, but never this silent. Everyone is motionless. Nobody stirs or speaks. Only their eyes flicker, reflecting lamplight, as they follow the Detective. She in turn murmurs a last remark to her officers, adds a note to her pad, then faces the gathering.

'Ladies and gentlemen, your patience is appreciated. But now the time has come to put an end to this inquiry. I have reached my conclusion.'

In the hush her fingernails click as they pick at the pages of her notebook. 'That our victim, like all the hedgehogs I have investigated, was unnaturally killed, we can have no doubt. The methods may be called murder by some, and that you can argue about among yourselves. I am here to establish facts and pinpoint the cause of death.'

The silence remains absolute.

'We heard first of the loss of hedgehog life from motor vehicles, and Mr Clarkson's pleas of innocence. Our victim could well have met her end beneath his wheels, but whether by accident or murder or contributing circumstance was the issue to be decided. And we have heard from Tommy Brock, who does not deny that he has been implicated before in hedgehog killings. Hedgehogs fear him. But does that make him responsible for murder, or is he too a victim of changed fortunes?'

She turns a page in her notebook. 'Then we come to Major Geddoff, who had much to say on many subjects, including on his own ill intentions towards Mr Brock. He has facilitated the eviction of hedgehogs from his property and watched as their food supplies dwindled, all in the pursuit of production efficiency. Major Geddoff argues these actions were unavoidable by-products of an embedded system, to which he and his tenants had little option but to subscribe. And lastly we have been thoroughly apprised of Ms Nymbies' excellent intentions towards the deceased: intentions belied by exclusionary domestic policies and an all-consuming love of home comforts that ironically left our victim with nowhere to live. Nothing deliberate, Ms Nymbies claims, but perhaps sufficient grounds for a charge of hog-slaughter, through negligence.'

The Detective takes a breath. 'Ladies and gentlemen, these matters are intricately intertwined. You all plead innocence, yet fail to *exonerate yourselves. But despite the complexities, I have reached my conclusion. The cause of this hedgehog's demise was—' She raises her chin, looks them in the eye. 'Well, it's the whole bleeding lot of you, isn't it?'*

The announcement, of course, is met with an outcry.

There it is, the terminal stop on Murder Road, the final twist of the blade, the big reveal. Yes indeed, there was no single murderer. It was everyone. Of course it was. And so it is tempting to conclude that the parlous state of British hedgehogs is the result of some sort of real-life *Murder on the Orient Express*, with every suspect contributing a knife stroke (albeit of varying strength), making them jointly and equally culpable. And it is true that the killers in life, as in fiction, will almost certainly walk free, permitted to do so by the forgiveness of a complicit society. But unlike the deceased in Agatha Christie's locomotive yarn, our hedgehog was blameless, having wronged nobody. There is no sense in which the death was a deserved fate. But likewise one could argue that there was little premeditation among any of our suspects.* The

---

* Sure, Tommy Brock certainly does snaffle the occasional hedgehog, and that probably doesn't happen by accident. This is an issue on

hedgehog died from circumstance, not intention. And so a more fitting literary equivalent perhaps lurks amid the tangle of conspiring circumstances portrayed by J. B. Priestley's *An Inspector Calls*. Perhaps the death was no murder but a damning indictment of society's failings. The dysfunction in each suspect's relationship with the hedgehog contributed to its demise. So no one can, or should, shoulder all of the blame.

Even in possession of all the facts, correctly apportioning responsibility is hard. That said, the different impacts are clearly not equal. The recent, widespread and unprecedented loss of hedgehogs' habitats, combined with the equally unprecedented depletion of invertebrate prey resources, could only ever constitute an immense blow to Britain's ability to sustain them. And while we cannot be certain how many of the effects of the rise in badger numbers are catalysed by the destruction of the hedgerows and the decimation of their joint prey base, the fact remains that the fear of badgers and predation by badgers demonstrably shape the current distribution of hedgehogs

---

which some hedgehog ecologists will disagree, but for me the telling point is that the badgers themselves will not have changed their behaviour in millennia. Something else is mediating their relationship with hedgehogs. And that's why I say there is no metaphorical intentionality.

nationally. Hedgehogs are found where badgers are not, and that is unlikely to be a coincidence. Agricultural intensification and badgers are plausibly sufficient to have caused between them the lion's share of hedgehog disappearances.

That said, hedgehogs are clearly not helped by the vast numbers of traffic deaths on our rural and suburban roads, nor by the fragmentation of their populations created by motorways. But had rural hedgehog habitats remained intact, even hundreds of thousands of annual road-killed hedgehogs might not have driven the population into decline. And in terms of barriers between populations, the vast tracts of now-empty agricultural land, bereft of the hedges that made it navigable, arguably represent a far more severe hurdle. Finally, there is the often fatal negligence with which hedgehogs are treated in parks and gardens. They die, certainly, from countless accidents, and their population sizes are limited by the increasing unsuitability and inaccessibility of urban habitats. But again, in isolation, these effects would probably be nowhere near sufficient to cause the national decline we have witnessed.

Nothing, though, is happening in isolation. Road casualties and urban hedgehog deaths no longer comprise a comparatively small proportion of national mortality. They are now an escalating risk afflicting the last survivors in some of the few habitats in which they can still cling on. The wider context converts a suite of minor concerns into an existential threat, particularly in villages, towns and cities. Strimmers, electric fences and now robot mowers are novel sources of death and danger to which hedgehogs cannot hope to evolve an adequate response* – and any one of which could prove to be the final straw.

Modern life has ganged up on a beloved animal.[†] And, with a grim inevitability, modern life is coming out on top. This is not an observation unique to hedgehogs. It applies to species across the wide surface of the Earth. Hedgehogs are simply a prominent victim, one that has come to our collective attention. When a species' numbers are collapsing, you'd think you'd notice. But actually, mostly, you don't. That's because the process appears deceptively gradual. The numbers one year are similar to the previous year, maybe even be a bit higher. But the trend over decades could still be dire. Humans don't

---

* Evolution works when a changed circumstance benefits some individuals that then go on to breed more successfully. It's rather difficult to envisage how any individuals might be sufficiently strimmer-proof to give them a competitive edge.

† A tip of the pen to Pat Morris for this observation.

live decade by decade. We live day by day. Immersed in our lives, the details of childcare, work, hobbies and bickering on social media mean that our attention is everywhere at once. Every so often we raise our heads, and only then do we find that something, somewhere has changed while we weren't looking.

When I was a kid I used to help my dad clean the car. If you're over the age of forty you'll probably remember doing the same, and trying to avoid being handed the sponge and bucket. The fun bit was being allowed to hold the hose, and discreetly aiming it at your brother when nobody was looking. The sponge meant you had to clean the numberplate and headlights. And those were forever coated in a wax-thick glued-on layer of splatted, then sun-baked insects. In much the same way that a dollop of dried Weetabix can only be removed with a hammer and chisel, dried car insects render a soapy sponge entirely inadequate for its intended purpose. Over the summer holidays, when we hit the road to visit relatives or to freeze ourselves to insensibility on a Norfolk beach,* the headlights needed cleaning every few weeks. But then, at

---

* My wife is Greek. I had to explain to her what a windbreak is, and why you might need one on a beach. You can only imagine the look of

some point between those days and these days, car headlight cleaning stopped being a job. I haven't done it in years. And I barely even find a dead insect on the car, now.

Things changed. And I failed to notice. It's not just me. I have spoken with many wildlife professionals who feel the same bewilderment I do at having not realized sooner that something serious had occurred. In fact, I have met only one person who wasn't taken by surprise. And that's because, over the two decades since he moved to his house in the Chilterns, Trevor Lawson has been running a nightly informal insect survey on the ceiling of his living room.

On a nice summer's evening Trevor sits with his windows open, watching the ceiling fill up with an assortment of moths, craneflies and generally exuberant six-legged aerial life. At the outset of his mini-experiment, on a good night, when the weather was right, he would get something like fifty to one hundred different insects buzzing and flapping and settling on the plaster. Now, twenty years on, it's down to twenty to forty. But that's not per night. That's *per week*. This is a single anecdote, with a non-standard methodology from one

---

horrified pity she gave me when I said that sometimes we'd shelter behind it to keep warm while eating ice-cream.

household in the Chilterns (surrounded on three sides by highly intensive arable farms).* But the point is clear – even in the relatively few years since the beginning of the twenty-first century, the quantity and diversity of flying insects entering Trevor's house has crashed.

Trevor's friend and neighbour Mike Collard isn't such an insect enthusiast, but he certainly loves birds. He has lived in the Chilterns for thirty-five years. When he moved in, his house had starlings nesting in the eaves. He would awaken every morning to their chatter. They stopped doing that about twenty-five years ago, and he has barely seen one in the last twelve. His pride and joy were the marsh tits that used to visit his garden. Other birders knew that if they visited Mike they could simply look out of his kitchen window, cuppa in hand, and be guaranteed a sighting. He saw them every day, right up until when he didn't. He gets one a month, now, if he's lucky. He has seen virtually no house sparrows for twenty years. Greenfinches have all but disappeared, along with goldfinches and coal tits. And on his regular local walk he now struggles to find birds. There should be tree sparrows, willow tits, spotted

---

* Your detecting instincts are correct. That parenthetical observation is indeed a clue to the causes.

flycatchers and whitethroats, but they're all nearly gone. He hasn't heard a whitethroat this year. There should, he says, be three on his walk. But as of the end of May he had heard none. And that means he now probably won't hear one at all this year.

To speak with Trevor and Mike is to be immediately struck by how passionate and knowledgeable they are about wildlife, especially in their local area. That knowledge has left both with a profound sense of sadness and loss. Nature that used to bring them daily happiness and pleasure has steadily drained from around their homes. They are watching it happen, in real time, seemingly powerless to prevent it. Their cherished wildlife is being lost.

Or, rather, it is being taken away.

Vanishing aerial invertebrates and vanishing birds are man-made phenomena. That the dwindling insect occupation of Trevor's ceiling and my recollections about bug-splats on numberplates are not mere 'anecdata' is borne out by recent work. The Bugs Matter citizen science survey, published in 2022, asked people to record the number of squashed invertebrates on their numberplates, in Kent in 2019 and nationwide in 2021. The researchers compared these results with those of a national survey using the same method in 2004. Over this period the number of insects on vehicle numberplates more than halved, falling by 59 per cent.

In 2017 a landmark paper examined the total biomass (i.e. the total combined weight) of insects over twenty-seven years (1989–2016) across sixty-three nature reserves in Germany. The choice of these protected areas is telling, because they should be unaffected by what is happening in the surrounding (mainly agricultural)* landscape. But what the paper found is absolutely horrifying to anyone who understands anything about ecology. The biomass of aerial insects declined by three-quarters in under thirty years. At the outset of the research, any one of the researchers' insect traps captured about 10g of insects per day. By the time it concluded, in 2016, this had fallen to about 2g. That loss of abundance is likely to be matched by a loss of diversity. The species richness of hoverflies, for example, is pretty well predicted by their biomass. So fewer and fewer insect species are being represented by fewer and fewer individuals. And if what is occurring in protected areas in Germany is representative of what's happening across Europe – which it almost certainly is – then a staggering tonnage of insects has vanished.

---

* Look, a clue, another clue!

What is true in Europe is true everywhere. A recent study of the global state of insects concluded with the words: 'This review highlights the dreadful state of insect biodiversity in the world, as almost half of the species are rapidly declining and a third are being threatened with extinction.'* The rates of loss were steep enough for the authors to predict that 40 per cent of the world's insect species will go extinct in the next few decades.

The consequences of this insect Armageddon ramify up the food chain. Imagine for a moment that instead of insects the traps in the German biomass study had been catching prime fillet steak.† Imagine that people need these traps to provide food for their own families. Over a hundred days in 1989 any given trap would have provided a family of four with 250g of steak each. Now they'd get 50g each. For insectivorous birds, this is not an abstract thought experiment. It's a

---

* You know things are going properly pear-shaped when scientists, publishing in top-flight academic journals, use value judgements like 'dreadful' in the text and the referees, who are generally the most pedantic people on the planet, just let them do it. That can only happen if the trends their study showed really *were* dreadful.

† Apologies to non-meat-eaters. Please substitute a protein-rich dietary item of your choice.

life-threatening assault on their food security. Yet another car-windscreen survey, this time in Denmark, showed an 80 per cent decline in flying insects between 1997 and 2007, but took it further, by demonstrating that the rate at which barn swallows feed their nesting young correlates with insect numbers. Fewer insects means less food going into young swallows. And that means fewer swallows around in general. Numbers of breeding pairs of house martins, barn swallows and sand martins vary with the amount of insects on cars.*

North America is estimated to have lost nearly three billion birds in forty-eight years – just under a third of all the birds that the country could support in the 1970s. And the worst affected are the insectivores. The losses are mirrored across Europe, where numbers of common bird species like house sparrows and starlings are spiralling downward at an alarming rate. Worse still, the majority of the decline in European birds is explicable by a few very common bird species experiencing

---

* As a sampling tool cars are a bit of a blunt instrument, but studies have shown that windscreen counts yield the same trends as other methods. So if no unlucky insects have become rather detailed diagrams of themselves on your bonnet, it's not because traffic has changed, or car aerodynamics have improved. It's what biodiversity loss in full swing looks like.

immense losses in numbers, while some rarer species are actually doing a bit better than they were. Rare species doing better is a good thing, certainly. But rare species tend to be confined to more specific types of habitat that are more easily targeted for conservation at the local level, for example in nature reserves. Rare species can buck a general trend. Common species are by definition widespread, so what happens to them is a telling indication of the quality of the wider environment. Starlings are in some ways the avian counterpart of hedgehogs. Neither are fussy animals. They can live in all sorts of places, under all sorts of conditions. And if these unfussy animals start to vanish, it's because of terrible background levels of ecological devastation.

We have already met the causes. The studies of insects, from the global to the local, are unanimous in blaming habitat loss caused by agriculture and urbanization, and pollution, mainly from synthetic pesticides and fertilizers. Even insects in nature reserves suffer from being surrounded by agricultural fields, which may act as a sort of insect-sink, sucking the life out of the reserves. Similarly, the wholesale depletion of grassland bird populations in North America arises through a combination of habitat loss and more toxic pesticide use in both breeding and wintering areas.

The events that have befallen hedgehogs in Britain are not some uniquely applicable, one-off case study. They are an in-depth illustration of the sort of processes afflicting species everywhere. Insects, birds, mammals: once-common wildlife is flowing away, lost to the combined forces of those two scally-wags, agricultural intensification and urbanization. These are implicated in conservation catastrophes across the board.

In 2016 researchers picked 8,688 species from over eighty-two thousand on the Red List of Threatened Species (the internationally recognized global standard for evaluating spe-cies' risk of extinction) compiled by the International Union for Conservation of Nature, and ranked the various conserva-tion ills that had befallen them. Most of the species picked, from all over the world, were birds, mammals and amphib-ians, the rest comprising fish, reptiles, flowering plants and invertebrates. While the single most common threat, affecting nearly three-quarters of all species, was overexploitation (mostly stemming from logging, with smaller contributions from hunting and fishing), the second largest hazard to bio-diversity was the conversion of wildlife habitats into agricultural areas, coupled with the intensification of existing agriculture. Agricultural conversion and intensification between them imperilled nearly two-thirds of all the species examined. Most of this was from crop farming (affecting about half of species) and livestock farming (affecting a quarter of species). Third on the list was urban development, which mainly stems from land conversion to meet the demand for housing. That threatened about a third of all species.

The greatest threats to biodiversity on planet Earth continue to arise from exploitation, agriculture and the expansion of cities. I say 'continue to' because since the year 1500 three-quarters of all the plants, mammals, amphibians, reptiles and birds that have gone extinct were harmed by overexploitation, agricultural activity, or a combination of both. Rampant urbanization is a modern factor thrown into an already corrosive mix. Together, these trends are driving extinction, and they are gathering pace.

That pace is driven in large part by the number of people in existence. The world population of humans more than doubled between 1961 and 2016. And the result is that demand for land for the production of food, feed and energy is still increasing. Serving that demand is approximately five billion hectares* of agricultural land (about one-third growing crops

---

* It's an area 2,500 times the size of Wales. It's as big as 6.1 billion football pitches. You're welcome.

and two-thirds pastures and meadows for livestock), representing about 38 per cent of the global land surface. But the
amount of cropland available per person alive has decreased
continuously from just under half a hectare each in 1961 to
around a fifth of a hectare each now. So to produce more food
for a growing population means either converting more wildlife habitat into agricultural land or wresting higher yields
from the land already in use. Very little unused fertile land is
left, so achieving future food security is likely to rely heavily
on agricultural intensification. This might sound like a
reprieve for wildlife, implying that we won't be converting any
more pristine habitats into crops, but that optimism fails to
consider two key points. First, just because the wildlife habitat we have left isn't very fertile, that doesn't mean people
won't go on logging and burning it anyway, just to get a few
years of cropping or grazing pasture out of it. And second, as
we have seen with hedgehogs, for wildlife the *intensity* of agriculture is a matter of life and death.

Over half of the world's cropland and pasture is still used at
low intensity. It relies on natural predators rather than chemicals, natural fertilization, rotated crop plants and low-density
herds. Increasing to medium intensity means monocultures,
targeted pesticides and natural fertilization. Increasing again

to high intensity means broad-spectrum pesticides, chemical fertilizers, multiple harvests every year, high grazing pressure. Each step squeezes more calories from a patch of land. But it also squeezes out wildlife. Moving from medium to high intensity, for example, increases yields by around 85 per cent. But intensification of agriculture is currently responsible for about a quarter of the current rates of loss of vertebrate bio-diversity globally. Which is a problem, given that it is the future path towards feeding the human world.

I am writing at the outset of a global food crisis. Hundreds of millions are going hungry as food costs skyrocket. Those costs in turn have responded to a heady mixture of rising fuel prices, fertilizer shortages and reduced wheat yields, brought about by the Russian invasion of Ukraine, as well as heavy rains in China that are predicted to ruin its winter wheat crop, a drought in the US that affected its last winter crop, floods in Australia and South Africa, and extreme heat in India, Pakistan and, most recently, Spain. In short, the delicate mix of economics and world affairs that influences the ability of the world to feed its citizens has been rocked by geopolitical events and climate change. And as a result, just ensuring that everyone receives enough nourishment to survive is becoming a critical challenge.

Now is not a good time to try to argue for conservation action. If conservation has one big ask, it's that we should give half of the surface of the Earth back to nature. It's a powerful, simple message that makes clear exactly what level of protection is needed to reduce, and perhaps halt, the onrushing extermination of global biodiversity. Anything less dooms species to extinction. But notwithstanding that nature provides vital ecosystem services on which everyone relies, in a food crisis, when land is needed to feed people, the idea of giving it to conservation starts to sound distinctly like trading in human lives.

Can we achieve the bold conservation goal enshrined in the Half-Earth policy without compromising our ability to feed everyone? Perhaps. But there are unavoidable trades-off.* Keeping agriculture and nature completely separate (i.e. having regions that do nothing but agriculture and regions that do nothing but nature) would result in big losses to humans, potentially amounting to about a third of cropland, just under

---

* Pedantry again, but I'm pretty sure this is the correct plural of 'trade-off', because it's multiple 'trades', not multiple 'offs' – in much the same way that the plural of 'court-martial' is 'courts-martial' because it's multiple 'courts' that happen to all be 'martial'. Or is it?

a half of pastureland, a quarter of non-food calories (i.e. stuff grown that humans don't eat, like biofuel and animal feed) and just under a third of food calories. That could lead to mass starvation. If, on the other hand, we allow landscapes to remain as mosaics of agriculture and wildlife habitat, Half-Earth would result in losses of about 15 per cent of cropland, 10 per cent of pastureland and 3 per cent of food calories. That is starting to sound feasible; but some countries would suffer more than others. Both China and India, which have the highest numbers of undernourished people on the planet, would suffer substantial drops in available food. There is no pathway to giving over half our planet to nature without at least some nations losing out, and so a prerequisite would be to ensure the protection of vulnerable, food-insecure populations.

Historically, we have not been brilliant at sharing food equitably across the globe. But there are clear benefits to our getting our collective act together. The prize is improved global levels of nutrition, improved population health, and the halting and reversal of biodiversity losses. The level of coordination this would demand, though, would be unprecedented in history. It would require corporations and governments to sign up to an overarching plan, and for all of us to make adjustments to our lives. There are three basic components of a plan to feed humans and save wildlife. The saving wildlife bit requires us to increase the extent and management of protected areas, as well as restoring habitats (e.g. through rewilding) and implementing landscape-level conservation planning. But without the remaining two components those actions would directly compete with food production. The second component is to ensure the supply of food. It means carefully and sustainably increasing crop yields, and coupling this with increased trade in agricultural goods to even out disparities between nations' ability to feed themselves. The final component is critical, and it is one that all of us individually will have to engage with, sooner rather than later. It's to reduce the existing demand for food. If we can get all three components working together, we really can feed everyone in the world and set the requisite conditions to allow us to preserve flourishing populations of wildlife.* That, right there, is a prize worth striving for.

Whether we attain it is in our hands, individually. Demand for some types of food is currently too high. The clearest example is beef. The collective result of beef-eating is staggering rates of forest loss. If we were to replace only a fifth of the

---

* It's tempting to say we can have our cake and eat it, but that might be in poor taste.

world's per-capita beef consumption with mycoprotein (which has similar protein quality to beef, in terms of provision of essential amino acids and digestibility, but requires far, far less land), by 2050 this would inhibit climate change by reducing methane emissions by 11 per cent, and would also bring projected rates of annual deforestation down by half. Going further, and swapping out half of the beef consumed per person, would result in a more than 80 per cent reduction in deforestation and carbon emissions. Eat less beef. It's really not a massive request of any one of us. In fact, it's incredibly easy, and the overall effect would be to preserve functioning natural ecosystems and reduce climate change.

And if we want to go further, there are diets we can adopt. They too are surprisingly non-stringent. The Planetary Health diet, for example, was formulated by thirty-seven different scientists working together for the EAT-Lancet Commission. It's a healthy, flexitarian diet, in which you elect to eat a lot of wholegrains, fruits, vegetables, nuts and legumes, with smaller proportions of meat and dairy. I have accidentally pretty much been eating this diet for years,* and, well, I like it. It's a lot

---

* I'd like to pretend that I adopted it off the back of a lot of research, because of my pristine environmental conscience and amazing

better for you, and a heck of a lot less expensive, than more meat-heavy diets. And it's also, as the name suggests, a lot better for the environment. If everyone in the US adopted this diet, for example, it would alleviate about 30 per cent of the threats to biodiversity that arise from the country's food consumption. And if the dietary shift were combined with the government and corporations putting in place strategies to

---

determination, and because I'm an organized and motivated individual. But that would be a lie. In truth, I'm a terrible cook and my wife is a very good cook who makes most of our meals. We decided to eat a bit less meat for ethical reasons, and to buy good quality fruit and veg. And this diet kind of emerged from that decision and her cooking ability. We have meat a few times a month, but my reading of the diet is that it would actually allow you to have more than that. If I'm doing exercise and feel like I need more protein, I usually just add some Quorn to my portion as an easy fix. Look, I'm six foot one with the metabolism of a hyperventilating rodent, I burn calories like nobody's business and I eat like a horse – and it works just fine for me. So it might be worth a go if you haven't tried it. (You may ask why I'm not promoting veganism, which after all would solve a lot of conservation and animal welfare problems. But I suspect it's just too big an ask of the majority of folks. Instead let's aim for an easy start, agreeing to do one or two very simple things upfront. If enough good people join in with those, then we will have collectively done well.)

remove half of avoidable food waste, it would essentially halve the threat to biodiversity.

I like the idea of being able to make a small personal change to help. When huge, systemic issues beset the world, they feel like they are far beyond our individual powers to influence. I know that feeling well. It's the daily burden of a conservation scientist – more than of many other occupations. You quickly gain a stark understanding of how vast the mountain of conservation problems is, compared with the pitifully tiny, underfunded trowel you have just been handed to try to level it. Personally, I deal with the angst by remembering that my job is not to change everything on my own. To borrow a metaphor from a eusocial insect, my job is to carry a carefully carved-out leaf-disc back to my ants' nest. I have to trust the other ants to do the same. If they do, we'll soon have a nice stream of leaf-discs flowing across the landscape and disappearing below ground. Once they're there, we can create a lovely leaf-mulch upon which to cultivate fungal treats for our larvae.* No one can feed the colony by themselves. But we can all carry a bit of leaf.

---

* You probably won't see a motivational speech like that in a self-help book. But you get what I mean.

Translating this into human terms, a minor dietary alteration is an easy, positive, step everyone can take to help. And with a little bit of a shove, this step can become a subtle, and then unsubtle, cultural shift. Nobody is asking for the impossible, or even for the terribly inconvenient. Nobody is demanding that everyone goes vegetarian or vegan (although the benefits of a vegetarian diet are slightly higher than those of the Planetary Health Diet). It's a case of eating less beef, consuming a bit less dairy and upping the amount of fruits, vegetables, fungi and grains in your shopping basket. And if we can alter the social norm of eating meat every single day, then between us we will be well on the way to upholding our side of the bargain. We will be helping to transform the food system, as a prerequisite for keeping conservation efforts from conflicting with food security. So, to paraphrase a First World War poster: Your Country Needs You [*to take a simple step to safeguard your own health by eating a few more vegetables and cutting down on red meat and dairy a little bit, thus enabling global conservation to make some headway against agricultural conversion and intensification and helping to ensure that everyone in the future has access to nature and ample supplies of good food*]!

All this just leaves urbanization to deal with. And guess what? There too we, individually and collectively, can make a sizeable, positive difference. The difference in this case is rewilding. And here I should again emphasize, as I did in my book *Elegy for a River*, that rewilding – especially urban rewilding – is not about turning your garden into a tangle of brambles, or asking your neighbours if they would be okay having wolves next door.

You can go the whole hog if you want to. Two of my friends did. Chris Sandom and his wife Lena are senior lecturers in conservation and zoology, respectively. When they moved home two years ago, they found themselves in possession of a 9 × 9m outdoor space that comprised a patio and a close-cropped lawn that stretched from fence to fence, with just a couple of tiny flowerbeds clinging on in the corners. There was a rose and a clematis and that was about it. Chris describes the garden as really boring and depressing. So they decided to rewild it.

In September 2020 they dug a wide bed encircling the whole of the outside of the lawn. Into this they introduced some shrubs and bushes, and a cherry tree, a pear tree and an aspen.* They sourced some of the shrubs from

---

* But then got nervous about how big the aspen might get, dug it up and put it into in a large pot instead. Just because folks are

neighbours who were throwing theirs out. Chris then got hold of the well-known gardening aid known as a 'sledge-hammer' and, in his words, channelled his inner wild boar all over the lawn. Literally going the whole hog allowed him to create tussocks and rip up turf before seeding the whole thing with yellow-rattle, a very handy wildflower that para-sitizes grass and stops it being too dominant. Once the yellow-rattle had established itself they could sow other wildflowers. Whenever they went for a walk they collected seeding plants, and when they got back shook the seeds into their own garden (a process Chris says mimics what aurochs would have done back when we had them in Brit-ain). And that was about it. In terms of additional maintenance it's a doddle. They kept the patio for barbe-cues, and for their kids they mow a ring around the lawn, so there's something akin to a racetrack through the shrubs and high grass. The rest is mostly allowed to grow, and just given the occasional late summer haircut to stop it getting too uppity.

Even for Chris, a rewilding expert, the results were

---

conservationists doesn't mean they get everything to do with nature right.

impressive. In less than a year the garden was utterly transformed, into something really quite beautiful. As the light changes throughout the day it catches leaves on the different shrubs and casts complex, dappled shadows that ripple in the breeze. The whole space immediately filled with invertebrate life, so wherever you look something is buzzing or scuttling or busying itself about. And the kids think it's amazing, the best place to crawl around or to play a game of hide-and-seek. But the highlight of everything, of course, was when the hedgehogs moved in. There had been no signs of them before, but now Chris's camera traps catch them most nights. The hedgehogs originally had to squeeze in under the gate, so Lena cut a nice hedgehog hole to make it easier. The garden offers all the food and shelter the hedgehogs could possibly want. Build it, or rather, let nature build it, and they will come.

What Chris and Lena did in a relatively small garden was extremely easy.* It's also really flexible. It works for wildlife and for people. They are planning to put in a fire pit, and

---

* Their experience resulted in a rather lovely pictorial guide, aimed at older children and explaining how to do the same. You can find it here: https://rewildingsussex.org/2022/07/28/a-wild-garden/.

might sometime mow the middle of the lawn for a bit, just to have the space. But you don't have to do anything on that scale if you don't want to. Anything green that you can nurture in your garden or patio, or on your windowsill, is still likely to have superb benefits for urban wildlife. Take pollinators as an example: we know that they are in decline, and that urbanization is a key reason. But at the same time, low-intensity urban sites (i.e. villages and green spaces) can actually have a higher diversity of pollinators than comparable natural vegetation. The difference between urban habitats full of pollinators and those that are contributing to a global decline is, yet again, *intensity*.

Urban intensity is the direct analogue of agricultural intensity, squeezing out space for wildlife. The highest urban intensities are associated with a decrease of 43 per cent in pollinator species richness and 62 per cent in their abundance, compared with the least intensive urban sites. But lot of that urban intensity is avoidable. It happens when green spaces get trimmed, mowed and manicured to within an inch of their (and everyone else's) lives. A lot of 'intensity' is much the same thing as 'tidiness' – the same tidiness that has ravaged hedgehog habitat across our farms and towns. Hedgehogs, of course, are again just a prominent example, representing thousands upon thousands of species that are suffering the indignity of being tidied to death.*

Tidiness takes a lot of effort. And it costs money that would be better spent doing almost anything else. As a result, conservation ecologists' collective desire to dismantle the cult of tidiness[†] has one major advantage: we want people to do less work, and spend less time and money, making their

---

* One of Chris and Lena's neighbours, for example, astroturfed their entire lawn, to make it nice and easy to maintain. Except it's not actually maintenance-free at all. They periodically have to clean the astroturf to stop it going mouldy. And that means buying some unpleasant chemical products and spraying them around and scrubbing the astroturf for a bit. To make that easier, you can now buy something that looks suspiciously like a lawnmower, called an 'artificial grass sweeper', so you can periodically give the ersatz grass an nice ersatz mowing. I hesitate to criticize anyone else's life choices but . . . *what in the name of all that's holy is the point in that?* Plus it will kill all of the invertebrate life beneath it, and probably smell terrible while the worms and everything are rotting. It costs money, creates rather than saves work, fills the world with plastic, destroys wildlife and looks awful. It's insane.

[†] Just for full disclosure, 'the cult of tidiness' is a phrase I've borrowed from Hugh Warwick.

surroundings look dull and boring. Nurturing wildlife is something we can all do right now. Step away from the lawnmower,
put your feet up and make a nice cup of tea. Do that for longer,
and you have helped wildlife more. The less work we put into
making our gardens neat, the more and more we are protecting
some of the most valuable resources on the planet.

Rewild even a tiny patch of your garden, balcony or
window-box, and you will be joining a budding movement.*
No Mow May, the campaign run by Plantlife, is cutting through
to the public consciousness. So much so that by the end of
May this year I really began to get the sense that we are turning
a corner in our national appreciation of nature in cities. Walk-
ing around my home city of Oxford, and visiting the city of
Bath, I have spotted mini-meadows springing from roadside
vegetation, and stands of grass and wildflowers left to flourish
in parks and public spaces. Whereas before they would have
been cut, now they are being left to do their twin jobs of looking gorgeous and harbouring wildlife. In doing so, they are
costing you and everyone else who pays taxes less than

---

* Literally. Hmmm. Maybe I need to speak to someone about the
punning.

nothing. They are saving your council money. And as more and more people understand the value of these oases, the more and more it will become not just acceptable but admirable to have patches of our own gardens filled to bursting with wildness. I fervently hope that this is the beginning of a modest revolution. One day, in my hoped-for future, those old-fashioned neighbours tut-tutting at the sight of a luxuriant, flower-and-bee-filled corner will be considered the height of self-destructive social weirdness. On that day, we will be open to nature again. And that is the best possible news for our children.

I grew up in the north-east of England in an odd little market town that until recently nobody had heard of.* It lies at the gateway to the bleak moorlands of Upper Teesdale and yet somehow manages to possess both a Norman castle and a French château. Because I was brought up there, I never really understood why it was unusual to have a château a hundred

---

* The town is called Barnard Castle, and these days is famous for reasons that can only be described as 'disappointing'. It has a blue plaque dedicated to Charles Dickens, who passed through occasionally. Some wit created another one that reads, 'Dominic Cummings was lurking in these parts' and nailed it to a wall. I'm proud of you, whoever you are.

metres away from your front door. Similarly, I never queried why we didn't get hedgehogs in our garden. This being the north, our garden was massive, and also surrounded by really thick, old stone walls (yes, just like Ms Nymbies'). At some point an accident befell the gate at the side of our house, and a bit of metal railing underneath it fell off. This meant that our dog could now sniff the feet of passers-by* – and, when I was about ten years old or so, a hedgehog wandered in off the street for a bit of an investigation. I spotted it in the evening as it was snuffling its way down our back yard towards the garden gate. And . . . I didn't know what to do. I wanted to marvel at it, but also to pick it up, make sure it was okay, convinced that it must have got lost or something. Because, well, *what was it doing there*? I naturally assumed that something, somewhere, had gone horribly wrong. It never occurred to me that our garden might be just what it wanted, and that given the smallest of encouragement we might have had loads of them on a nightly basis.†

---

* And scare the living daylights out of them by barking unexpectedly from below knee height.

† There is a rather telling follow-up to this story. Literally a fortnight after I wrote this, my mother delightedly told me that she'd seen a

It is thirty-six years since that happened, but I can still recall my feeling of smitten fascination. I ran to my mother, seeking her reassurance that all would be okay for the little hedgehog. She advised me just to leave it be, which was good advice. There are two points to this story. The first is that wild creatures bring magic into a life. I reacted with a child's enthusiasm to the hedgehog because I was a child. But this morning I watched a video sent to me by Chris, showing the hedgehog squeezing under his gate, having a good scratch and meandering away – and now I am writing this filled with the same childish delight that I felt then. I'm desperate for my little daughter to come home from nursery so I can show her the video, and say: 'Look at this hedgehog, isn't that just wonderful?' She loves watching birds and squirrels as they visit our garden, and I know she'll love the hedgehog. And more than anything I want her to be able to see a hedgehog for real, and

---

hedgehog in our back yard again. The first in *decades*. It had trundled in (you guessed it) under our gate. (My parents have put in hedgehog holes, but they are in a minority and so this hedgehog was using the pavement to navigate.) And then, just one week later she sent me another message that read, 'Bloody, bloody hell. Just scraped a squashed hedgehog off the road outside.' And that, in a nutshell, is the tale of urban hedgehogs.

say to her that hedgehogs in the garden are going to be part of her heritage, because we took some easy steps to make it happen.

But I can't. Not yet. And the risk, if we don't manage it, is that her baseline will be permanently altered. Just as I never expected to see a hedgehog, neither shall she. And neither shall a generation of children expect to see any of the plants and animals that they should be able to marvel at as their birthright. The lack of wildlife that I, born in the latter half of the twentieth century, experience as 'normal' would be regarded as a horrific aberration by anyone living in the preceding 99.99 per cent of human history. And yet my own experience is likely to be far, far richer than that of my daughter. Something within me aches to think that she may never know how much more delight-filled her life could – and should – be.

I have hope, though. We are talking about declining nature, not extinct nature. Nothing, yet, is a *fait accompli*, and everything is mitigable. The timeframe in which plants and insects can bounce back is incredibly short. Get that sorted, and the birds and hedgehogs will follow. And the best news is that you and I can influence proceedings. We began our hedgehog story with news of a political 'charge' to preserve them. That charge has not yet resulted in any change in legislation in the hedgehogs' favour. Among many unfortunate ramifications of that lack, newly developed housing still comes with no obligation for developers to consider the impacts on hedgehogs. But that doesn't mean there's nothing anyone can do.

While writing this, I heard two inspiring stories that both involved letters. The first letter was sent by a man called Jonathan Houseago.* His tale is very simple. Jonathan is retired and lives on a housing estate. He realized he was getting hedgehogs in his garden so he began feeding them. Then he found the Hedgehog Highways group on Facebook and was inspired to install some highways of his own. And then he realized that there were three housing developments in his local area that would end up converting a lot of farmland to homes, effectively removing some habitats and blocking access to some others, all possibly endangering the local hedgehog population. So he rang up the head office of each of the three developers and sent them very polite emails asking them to be considerate builders. In response one developer agreed to cut about a hundred hedgehog highways in the new

---

* Aka 'The Hedgehog Highwayman', as he was named by Folk Features in 2020. Why do I never get a cool nickname?

fences. Another agreed to raise the heights of the gates, to permit access. The third brushed off the requests. Jonathan persisted, again very politely. He kept sending letters until the third developer gave in, and agreed to install seventy-five hedgehog highways. Jonathan then started work on a leaflet to distribute to the new homeowners, telling them why the holes were so important. One man, through polite persistence and the act of writing some letters, made progress that has sadly eluded the brave instigator of the political charge to save hedgehogs.

The second inspiring story concerns a letter written by a seven-year-old girl called Gracie. She sent a big handful of rubber bands she had collected off the street, with a letter, to her local Royal Mail sorting office. It said: 'Please may your postmen and women stop dropping the rubber bands. I picked all these up today on my way from school . . . Birds, foxes and hedgehogs think they are worms and eat them and die.' In response the Royal Mail reminded its staff that rubber bands should be kept for re-use. It's a small thing, a simple thing, but it might just prevent some hedgehogs from meeting an avoidable and really nasty fate.

We need more of this sort of intervention. Just imagine what could happen if more people took a little time to do similar small things. What if we waged quiet, polite campaigns to ask for decent subsidies for farmers to reinstate hedgerows, or to manage those that have fallen into disrepair. What if, quietly and politely, we helped our farmers to cut down on agrochemicals, by voting with our wallets for high-quality, fairly priced produce that ensures they see a profit from their work? Or wrote polite letters to our supermarkets enquiring why increasing proportions of the fresh fruit we're supposed to eat to be healthy are now contaminated with the most hazardous types of pesticides – and what they intend to do about it, please? What if we, quietly and politely, wrote to our representatives on the town council, or to our local MPs, asking them to support initiatives to plant street trees and wildflower patches, to reduce traffic and to manage road verges with biodiversity in mind? What if we all left a few wild patches, chatted with our neighbours, and cut some holes in our shared fences?*

---

* I pose these questions knowing exactly how busy our lives are, and how the cost of living crisis makes everything harder, including opting to buy Fairtrade or organically farmed produce. With respect to the latter, I balance the costs by eating less meat and shopping at our local farmers' market. With respect to the former, I have a toddler and apparently, therefore, no time for anything that isn't feeding a toddler,

If there is one unresolved question at the end of our murder mystery, it is how long we are willing to remain reluctantly complicit in the types of circumstances that have led to the hedgehog's disappearance. Because we have the opportunity not to be. Hedgehogs, I admit, make for unlikely guides, but nevertheless we should take seriously what they have revealed to us. They are fantastically adaptable, and within living memory were busily delighting people almost everywhere. When species like that begin to suffer, we absolutely must take notice. Because the causes can only be systemic, pervasive and severe. They are causes that endanger not only wildlife but also our own health, and the very ecosystem services upon which all human well-being depends.

They are causes, however, that are far from irreversible.

---

playing with a toddler, cajoling a toddler into please putting down the breakable item, changing a toddler's nappy or full-on pleading with a toddler when she's decided that wearing a nappy full of poo is an unassailable human right. I also occasionally try to do some writing and research. There is a good reason why people joining movements tend to be either relatively young, or older and retired. Everyone in the middle is trying to juggle all sorts of ridiculousness while staying something like sane. But if we each do what we have capacity for, nobody can ask for a lot more.

To follow in hedgehogs' bumbling steps is to be led to understand that our homes, gardens and fields can and should be more diverse and verdant. To get us there, we can each embrace a handful of minor changes to our busy lives – changes that will improve our health and enhance our homes, that will cost us little and save us time. We can eat a little differently, and undertake constructive untidiness in patches of our gardens. We should perhaps be willing to pay a little more for good-quality farm produce that will support those farmers who are working in partnership with wildlife. We can be politely persistent when we see something that requires changing. And it really could be as simple as that. In so enhancing our own lives, we will help wildlife. Or perhaps it is the other way around.

To fail to act is to risk being left with little but fading memories – ghost hedgehogs in tattered hedgerows. But if we care enough for Britain's most beloved animal to make the few, small alterations needed to save it, then we too shall reap rewards.

The Detective watches as the guests disperse in various states of indignation and thoughtfulness. Her officers finish their business and then they too begin to depart. There is little left to do now but write the report. With such a plethora of contributing factors, it will probably just state that the deceased was a victim of circumstances beyond any one individual's control. It doesn't sit well with her. But not all murders, it seems, have a murderer.

She puts on her coat and walks to her car. She fumbles with the key-fob. The lights flash, the car unlocks. And at the sound, something in a nearby hedge startles. The Detective's head snaps towards the movement. Instinctively she drops, and crouches. She reaches for a torch, then hesitates. Breathing quietly, she waits and watches.

Leaves shake a little. Something rustles. A pause. The Detective catches the faintest hint of a snuffling, grumbling noise. Then she grabs the torch, and shines it full beam at the vegetation.

'Who's there?' she demands.

For an instant, beady eyes shine back at her. Then, with the merest hint of rotundity and spininess, whatever it was vanishes from view. The Detective fancies she hears a crackle of leaves and the patter of a creature speeding away. And then quietness and stillness descend once more. The Detective shakes her head. She stands, opens the car door, gets in, and drives away into the gathering dusk.

In the grounds of the Hotel Furzehoge the night air grows darker. And the hedgerows, for now, remain empty even of ghosts.

ONE FINAL WORD . . .

If you, or anyone you know, has been affected by issues raised in this book, then . . . well, that's great! Hedgehogs, and wild-life in general, need our help. And if you want to play a part in reversing the plight of our spiny friends, there are a lot of small, fun, easy things you can do. Much of this is stuff we can do at home, which has the advantage of making our houses look lovely, and amusing the kids. Some stuff, however, does involve dipping the smallest of toes into political waters.

To deal with the political bit first, at the local level there will be council candidates who want to implement green policies such as regulating the mowing of some public spaces, creating wildflower patches, sponsoring urban trees and making inter-ventions to benefit pollinators, birds, bats, you name it. They need your support. Please vote for them, and write letters to other councillors making clear that you value any initiative to green up our urban spaces and protect wildlife, from insects up. Beyond the local, any national political party that thinks it can simply ignore the looming biodiversity and climate-change crises while pursuing a business-as-usual model is, frankly, deluded. Please don't vote for the ostriches. (Meaning meta-phorical ostriches – you can vote for actual ostriches by not voting for the metaphorical ones.)

And while we're on large-scale stuff, I have touched on food waste, which is an issue that has very real implications in terms of using land that could otherwise belong to wildlife, and in terms of contributing to climate change. There are plenty of online guides for cutting down food waste at home, and almost anything we all do there will be a big benefit. And again, letters to supermarkets and MPs asking them what they're doing to address the problem are likely to be incredibly helpful.

In terms of fun stuff we can do specifically for hedgehogs, I took the liberty of asking several of the hedgehog folks I have spoken with what they'd really like to tell people from their experience. Below is what they said. Some of it is rather lovely.

DAVID WEMBRIDGE

I'd like people to record hedgehog sightings. And that goes for any wildlife, I think. It's not just because the data are so valuable to conservation; it's also that the process of stopping, taking a little bit of time out to look at your local environment and put it down on paper or the computer, just changes your perspective so much and puts you there, in your environment. You see things differently and begin to respond differently. It seems to me a really nice way to get into that appreciation of the natural environment, and you'll find your own aspects you're interested in. Just look, take time and tell people what you see, because that's really valuable; and it's also, I think, like mindfulness, a moment of just taking a little bit of time out to look at something.

We sometimes think of a hedgehog that visits our garden as belonging to just that one little spot. We don't appreciate that these hedgehogs might wander for miles, or that the hedgehog in our garden actually might be eight different hedgehogs – and there's this whole community and wider landscape and it's all connected, and we're fitting into a bigger landscape. You don't need a big wild garden to make a difference. Any little patio with pots is fine. That can all encourage invertebrate biodiversity and getting birds in, all sorts of things. Again, we need to get talking to our neighbours. Think about hedgehogs moving between gardens, think about this bigger local environment. It might be the park down the road, there might be a mill pond or something. But take responsibility for that wider environment as well, and because it's yours as much as anyone's.

HUGH WARWICK

Talk to your neighbour. It's all about communication and connection for wildlife, as it is between us and other human beings. So you say [to your neighbour], how about we join up our gardens? The only good reasons not to are a small tortoise or small dachshund. If you grow your own vegetables and need to make your garden rabbit-proof, you can still have a rabbit-proof channel, or a corridor the hedgehogs can use. So the first thing you're doing is opening up your garden. The second thing you are doing is destroying the cult of tidiness in your garden and then in your neighbours'. And then the other thing is to look wider still – but only a few people will have the capacity to do this. Not everyone can keep on top of planning in their area, but if you see a notice going up, or a piece in the local news, then just communicate with the developers. There is so little reason to not put in hedgehog highways, and eventually we will get to the point where enough developers have put in hedgehog highways that they will understand that this is going to be asked, and know that if they don't want to be seen in a bad light then they will have to start to treat this animal as if it has full legal protection.

SOPHIE RASMUSSEN

If people could be aware that they are sharing habitats with the hedgehogs, a lot of these issues would solve themselves. And then, let your garden grow wild. I mean, you could always blame it on the hedgehogs. I have an immensely wild garden because I want to help the hedge-hogs. It's not that I'm lazy or anything, but I want to help the hedgehogs. Because if you do let your garden get more wild and attract biodiversity, then there will also be natural nesting sites, and so on.

Also, be aware that everything we do will have an impact on nature and wildlife. Make sure a hedgehog can actually enter your garden – otherwise, whatever you do inside it will be worthless. This is a huge issue in Brit-ain. It doesn't happen in Denmark because they don't have these massive fences, they have hedges, and so hedgehogs can travel between gardens. But in the UK you have these long narrow gardens and high fences so hedgehogs can't even enter.

CARLY PETTETT

Think about diversity when planning your garden. Hedgehogs like a bit of everything; mowed habitats where worms are easy picking, longer grass and scrub for nesting and hiding, linear features to walk along, places to drink from, and little nooks and crannies for hibernating such as compost heaps, and under sheds. So, the more different habitats the better (including a treat of wet pet food from time to time too!). It's amazing where hedgehogs can squeeze in to nest, so be careful when disturbing wilder areas or piles of garden waste.

LAUREN MOORE

Hedgerows are a hedgehog's best friend (they aren't called hedgehogs for nothing), and particularly in rural areas where hedgehogs are struggling, having hedgerows and wild borders around fields is one of the best ways to support hedgehogs. They provide the vital combination of food and shelter (almost all of the hedgehogs I've monitored have nested in hedgerows at least once), as well as helping hedgehogs move throughout the landscape. The same goes for gardens – having one or all of the garden boundaries as hedgerows provides a valuable, connected network of green space, helping hedgehogs find the mates and food they need to thrive while giving hedgehogs fewer reasons to cross risky roads.

PHILLIP BAKER

First, get to know your neighbours. Ultimately, hedgehogs need a series of interconnected gardens, and this can only come from people working together. And creating neighbourhood communities is also likely to have positive benefits in other ways. Not everyone will end up helping, but you will be surprised how many people like to talk about hedgehogs; the trick is getting those people to do something positive. And that is perhaps more likely if they know you.

Second, allow a little bit of your garden to go wild. It doesn't have to be very much, and it doesn't have to be unattractive. But do find out a little bit about what invertebrates hedgehogs are dependent on, and garden accordingly. Assuming that hedgehogs can get into people's gardens, that's something that's going to make a difference. You can also help hedgehogs by putting out food (but make sure that it is suitable) and water, or creating a (hedgehog-safe) pond. Hedgehogs also readily use 'hedgehog boxes' for resting, hibernating and even breeding. You can even use a remote camera to watch their antics.

Last, get to know where your local hedgehog rehabilitator is. The more people you talk to, the more likely they are to contact you when they find an injured hedgehog (and hedgehogs always seem to find ways to get into trouble) and want to know what to do. Hedgehog rehabilitators also often want volunteer helpers, so if you have some spare time, you may be able to help get these animals back on their feet.

The numbers of hedgehogs going into wildlife hospitals are huge, and the sad thing is that it's mostly because of the same problems we already knew about in the 1980s: garden strimmers, drowning in ponds, getting caught in nets, rat poison, etc. It's all the same stuff, but bigger numbers. Which essentially means that as a society we haven't really learnt anything – which is disappointing. The challenge is therefore to find new ways to get the message out.

ABI GAZZARD

One of the most special things about hedgehogs is that they share a space with us. There aren't many other big conservation species that just stroll through your garden and which you can interact with, so they're really special in that way and we need to protect them so our children can see hedgehogs in their gardens. And they serve to encourage people to get involved beyond hedgehog conservation. The first port of call is to make your garden more accessible, but also we have to go above our insecurities and talk to our neighbours and encourage them to make their gardens more accessible as well. And I think it's so important to engage the public with protecting this kind of species, because it's the perfect opportunity to get people involved in some sort of conservation, and it would open up their eyes to enjoying wildlife and conserving other kinds of wildlife.

Also, try to enjoy hedgehogs without disturbing them – if they're well, they probably just want to be left in peace. It's usually quite obvious if a hedgehog is sick because they can have quite vocal symptoms, and if they're underweight they don't look right. They're usually a nice round ball, but if they're underweight they're diamond-shaped when curled up, so it's really easy to see.

RICHARD YARNELL

If you come across a hedgehog, I would think carefully before taking it to rehabilitation. You need to be absolutely certain it's ill and in need of care. There is a possibility that many healthy hedgehogs are taken to rehabilitation unnecessarily. And it's fine if you go to a reputable rehabilitator, who can tell whether the individual needs care, but I generally just say let wildlife be wildlife. These are wild animals after all. We can help hedgehog populations flourish by giving them the right conditions. And it is up to us to make sure they have the right conditions for them to persist.

Everything fits into the wider narrative of wildlife-friendly gardens. Things like artificial grass are just an abomination. In a world where there's a clear agenda about understanding and appreciating the environment and ecosystem services, if we could all just sort out our gardens that would be wonderful. And if we could use [people's love of] hedgehogs to get rid of artificial grass that would be brilliant. And there's a chance – if any species can do it, it's hedgehogs.

HEDGEHOG STREET'S GRACE JOHNSON

Helping hedgehogs doesn't need to be onerous or costly; the simplest garden changes can bolster vulnerable populations. Our Hedgehog Street campaign was launched to help anyone who would like to get involved, from newcomers through to seasoned wildlife gardeners – and even those without a garden. We currently have over 117,000 Hedgehog Champions and provide free resources including posters, leaflets and factsheets to spread the word, as well as interactive garden quizzes and forums. Alongside direct action in the garden for our prickly pals, a conversation can go a long way; chat hedgehog and it might just spark someone's interest. Hedgehogs are a brilliant flagship species; the 'cute factor' gets people interested, then garden additions like wild patches and log piles will benefit a plethora of other species too. So don't be surprised if you're rewarded with birds, butterflies and bats alongside hedgehogs.

PAT MORRIS

Hedgehogs have been around for millions of years, but now face increasing pressures from human development, with many different threats ganging up on them. It's important for us all to recognize the threats they face and to do our best to avoid making things worse. Better still, we can do things to help by making our gardens hedgehog-friendly. Even if we have no garden, we can ask park managers and those who look after playing fields, golf courses and allotments to help the hedgehogs that may use their land at night. Farmers and the people who mow road verges all need to 'think hedgehog'. You can check out the Hedgehog Street website for good ideas about ways to help these animals, and sign up to join the ever-increasing band of Hedgehog Champions. See what's on other social media too, but beware of bad advice from opinionated private 'experts' who have no affiliation with a recognized organization. The British Hedgehog Preservation Society is a reliable source of advice.

So there you have it: a smorgasbord of excellent hedgehog advice from folks who know. To this I will add that if you want to feed hedgehogs in your garden, meat-based wet dog, cat or kitten food will be very welcome, or you could perhaps opt for some of the speciality hedgehog foods available from supermarkets (although these are not regulated by anyone, so buyer beware). It turns out that the traditional bread and milk isn't a great combination, because the hedgehogs don't get a lot of nutrition from the bread, and they're lactose intolerant – so these are best avoided, unless you particularly want your flowerbeds full of hedgehog diarrhoea. Please also remember to leave out some water. There is further advice available on the Hedgehog Street and British Hedgehog Preservation Society websites, including on how to create nifty feeding stations out of plastic boxes and duct tape. But also remember that supplemental feeding is intended to be supplemental. Hedgehogs will mainly eat invertebrates, so please try to make your garden as friendly as possible to the slithery and crawly brigade.

Do consider getting involved with Hedgehog Street and becoming a Hedgehog Champion. Hedgehog Street is a joint initiative between the People's Trust for Endangered Species and the British Hedgehog Preservation Society, and has enough fun resources to keep kids (and adults) amused for days on end, doing things like building hedgehog houses. If you don't want to build one of those yourself, the British Hedgehog Preservation Society sells some, along with some rather cool 'hedgehog highway' signs that you can attach to your fence, as well as other amazing hedgehog-related products. All the money they raise goes towards hedgehog conservation. Their website also has a lot of amazing information and resources.

On the topic of wildlife-friendly gardening, it really is enjoyable to venture down that horticultural rabbit hole. You can get busy with bee hotels, bird boxes, wildflower patches and wood piles, and you'll be amazed at what wildlife you will soon start uncovering in even the teeniest of urban spaces. Again there is a plethora of guides online. And if you're like me, once you've made your peace with the adorably ramshackle rewilded bits, however tiny, you'll start to find so much more joy there than before. If you can encourage a few other folks to get involved, you will be giving the Tiggy-Winkles of this world the best possible opportunity to thrive. While I cannot guarantee that your efforts will be rewarded with a snuffly visitation, there's something deeply lovely about knowing that your actions are helping to shape a future in which maybe, just maybe, they will be.

NOTES

CHAPTER 1: MURDER MOST HORRID

7 'all laminated together against the cold': Pat Morris,
Hedgehog, The New Naturalist Library (Collins, 2018), p. 280;
D. W. Macdonald and P. Barrett, *Mammals of Britain and Europe*,
Collins Field Guide, 5th edn (Collins, 1993), p. 24.

7 'dropped to little more than half a million': Here's a
selection of the more credible sources. There are a *lot* more to
choose from: https://www.bbc.co.uk/news/uk-england-devon-
35122077; https://www.bbc.co.uk/newsround/48191799; https://
www.yourmag.co.uk/blog/hedgehogs-are-about; https://
wildlifeworld.co.uk/pages/hedgehogs; https://www.countryfile.com/
wildlife/10-of-the-most-endangered-animal-species-in-britain/;
https://www.dailymail.co.uk/news/article-2273572/where-
hedgehogs-gone-in-1950s-Britain-36-million-now-fewer-million-.
html.

**7 'Numbers are estimated to have halved between 2000 and
2018':** And yet more credible sources: https://uk.news.yahoo.com/
hedgehog-numbers-british-countryside-halved-past-18-years-
103147005.html; https://www.bbc.co.uk/news/science-
environment-42959766; https://www.thesun.co.uk/news/

5518353/rural-hedgehog-numbers-drop/; https://www.theguardian.
com/environment/2018/feb/07/hedgehog-numbers-plummet-by-
half-in-uk-countryside-since-2000; https://www.independent.
co.uk/climate-change/news/stop-hedgehog-disappearing-british-
gardens-forever-a8153581.html; https://theecologist.org/2017/
dec/18/how-we-can-help-our-hedgehogs-after-more-decade-
declining-numbers.

CHAPTER 2: DRIVEN TO DESTRUCTION

16 'Traffic has surged year on year': *Transport statistics Great
Britain: 2011* (Department of Transport, 2011), https://assets.
publishing.service.gov.uk/government/uploads/system/uploads/
attachment_data/file/8995/vehicles-summary.pdf.

16 'almost thirty-three million in 2020': *Number of licensed cars in
the United Kingdom (UK) from 2000 and 2020* (Statista, 2022),
https://www.statista.com/statistics/299972/average-age-of-cars-
on-the-road-in-the-united-kingdom/.

16 'plummeted to 1,550,000 in 1995': From Stephen Harris, Pat
Morris, Stephanie Wray and Derek Yalden, *A review of British
mammals: population estimates and conservation status of British
mammals other than cetaceans* (Joint Nature Conservation
Committee, 1995), p. 12.

16 'our most recent estimate': F. Mathews, L. M. Kubasiewicz,
John Gurnell, C. A. Harrower, Robbie A. McDonald and R. F.
Shore, *A review of the population and conservation status of British
mammals* (Natural England, 2018), p. 8.

16 '230,000 hedgehog road deaths': D. E. Wembridge, M. R. Newman, P. W. Bright and P. A. Morris, 'An estimate of the annual number of hedgehog (*Erinaceus europaeus*) road casualties in Great Britain', *Mammal Communications* 2, 2016, pp. 8–14.

16 'around 39 per cent of our hedgehogs between 1995 and 2018': Mathews et al., *A review of the population and conservation status of British mammals*, p. 8.

19 '"derived largely from guesswork"': Harris et al., *A review of British mammals*, p. 12.

20 '"during an evening's stroll in Kew Gardens"': Pat Morris, *Hedgehog*, The New Naturalist Library (Collins, 2018), p. 276.

23 'relatively few or quite a lot, really; who knows?': S. Croft, A. L. M. Chauvenet, G. C. Smith, 'A systematic approach to estimate the distribution and total abundance of British mammals', *PLoS ONE* 12, 2017, e0176339.

23 'just two out of five': Mathews et al., *A review of the population and conservation status of British mammals*.

29 'boasted of killing thirty a night with dogs': M. Burton, *The Hedgehog* (Andre Deutsch, 1969), p. 111.

29 'numbers killed per unit area decreased by 48 per cent': P. A. Davey and N. J. Aebischer, *Participation of the National Gamebag Census in the mammal surveillance network* (Joint Nature Conservation Committee, 2006), p. 26.

31 'fell from 174 in the former year to 21 in the latter': Nicholas J. Aebischer and Julie A. Ewald, *Trends and distribution of hedgehogs reported to GWCT's National Gamebag Census from 1981 to 2019: a* *report to the People's Trust for Endangered Species*, Game and Wildlife Conservation Trust, 2021, https://www.gwct.org.uk/media/1245072/NGC_Hedgehog_Report_to_PTES_2021.pdf.

31 'the game-bag data are suggestive of a decline': R. E. Whitlock, N. J. Aebischer and J. C. Reynolds, *The National Gamebag Census as a tool for monitoring mammal abundance in the UK: a report to the Joint Nature Conservation Committee* (Game Conservancy Trust, 2003), pp. 1–59.

32 'a 66 per cent decline in hedgehogs between 1995 and 2007': S. Roos, A. Johnston and D. Noble, *UK hedgehog datasets and their potential for long-term monitoring*, research report no. 598 (British Trust for Ornithology, 2012), pp. 1–63.

32 'a 77 per cent decline in hedgehogs between 2002 and 2019': D. Wembridge, G. Johnson, N. Al-Fulaij and S. Langton, *The state of Britain's hedgehogs 2022* (People's Trust for Endangered Species, 2022), p. 4.

33 'a decrease in hedgehog occupancy of England of about 5–7 per cent': A. R. Hof and P. W. Bright, 'Quantifying the long-term decline of the West European hedgehog in England by subsampling citizen-science datasets', *European Journal of Wildlife Research* 62, 2016, pp. 407–13.

36 'counted 5,321 dead hedgehogs': Morris, *Hedgehog*, p. 280.

37 'an average of 2.05 hedgehogs per 100km': Wembridge et al., 'An estimate of the annual number of hedgehog (*Erinaceus europaeus*) road casualties in Great Britain'.

40 'barriers to hedgehog movements': C. Rondinini and C. P. Doncaster, 'Roads as barriers to movement for hedgehogs', *Functional Ecology* 16, 2002, pp. 504–9.

41 'correlation between road casualties and numbers in the wider landscape': See papers cited in P. W. Bright, Z. Balmforth and J. L. Macpherson, 'The effect of changes in traffic flow on mammal road kill counts', *Applied Ecology and Environmental Research* 13, 2015, pp. 171–9.

41 'places where hedgehog numbers decreased': C. E. Pettett, P. J. Johnson, T. P. Moorhouse and D. W. Macdonald, 'National predictors of hedgehog *Erinaceus europaeus* distribution and decline in Britain', *Mammal Review* 48, 2018, pp. 1–6.

41 'the more of both species get hit by cars': Bright et al., 'The effect of changes in traffic flow on mammal road kill counts'.

42 '"at risk from collisions with vehicles"': Bright et al., 'The effect of changes in traffic flow on mammal road kill counts'.

42 'simply led to more of each species being hit': C. Grilo, F. Z. Ferreira and E. Revilla, 'No evidence of a threshold in traffic volume affecting road-kill mortality at a large spatio-temporal scale', *Environmental Impact Assessment Review* 55, 2015, pp. 54–8.

44 'sadly totalled 6,384 people': For 2021, see https://www.gov.uk/government/statistics/reported-road-casualties-in-great-britain-provisional-estimates-year-ending-june-2021; for 2020, see https://www.gov.uk/government/statistics/reported-road-casualties-great-britain-annual-report-2020/; for 2019, see https://assets.publishing.service.gov.uk/government/uploads/system/uploads/attachment_

data/file/922717/reported-road-casualties-annual-report-2019.pdf;
for 2018, see https://assets.publishing.service.gov.uk/government/
uploads/system/uploads/attachment_data/file/820562/Reported_
road_casualties_-_Main_Results_2018.pdf.

44 'likely to fall between 167,000 and 335,000': Wembridge et al., 'An estimate of the annual number of hedgehog (*Erinaceus europaeus*) road casualties in Great Britain'.

45 'differences of 35 per cent or greater': M. P. Huijser and P. J. Bergers, 'The effect of roads and traffic on hedgehog (*Erinaceus europaeus*) populations', *Biological Conservation* 95, 2000, pp. 111–16.

46 'Sweden (80 per cent males) and Ireland (64 per cent males)': See papers cited in L. J. Moore, S. O. Petrovan, P. J. Baker, A. J. Bates, H. L. Hicks, S. E. Perkins and R. W. Yarnell, 'Impacts and potential mitigation of road mortality for hedgehogs in Europe', *Animals* 10, 2020, p. 1523.

CHAPTER 3: THE TALE OF TOMMY BROCK

53 'no hedgehogs have visited for a couple of weeks': https://
kirtlingtonvillage.co.uk/kirtlington-hedgehog-street; https://
kirtlingtonvillage.co.uk/wp-content/uploads/2020/07/Hedgehogs-
Disappearance-in-Kirtlington-paper-FINAL-25-07-2020.pdf.

54 '200m or more away from buildings': K. A. Lee, *Untangling the roles of prey availability, habitat quality and predation as predictors of hedgehog abundance*, PhD dissertation, Nottingham Trent University, 2021, p. 173.

55 'one of the driest – and the sunniest – on record': https://
www.metoffice.gov.uk/about-us/press-office/news/weather-and-
climate/2020/2020-spring-and-may-stats.

55 'a lack of rain, especially early in the year': P. Nouvellet,
C. Newman, C. D. Buesching and D. W. Macdonald, 'A multi-
metric approach to investigate the effects of weather conditions on
the demographic of a terrestrial mammal, the European badger
(*Meles meles*)', *PLoS One* 8, 2013, e68116, https://doi.org/10.1371/
journal.pone.0068116.

56 'a particularly nasty parasitic infection': See D. W.
Macdonald, C. Newman, C. D. Buesching and P. Nouvellet, 'Are
badgers "Under the Weather"? Direct and indirect impacts of
climate variation on European badger (*Meles meles*) population
dynamics', *Global Change Biology* 16 (11), 2010, pp. 2913–22.

57 'a haven for songbirds': Cristina Eisenberg, 'Living in a
landscape of fear: how predators impact an ecosystem', *Scientific
American*, 13 Aug. 2010, https://www.scientificamerican.com/
article/predators-create-landscape-of-fear/.

58 'time spent avoiding getting browsed': J. W. Laundré,
L. Hernández and K. B. Altendorf, 'Wolves, elk, and bison:
reestablishing the "landscape of fear" in Yellowstone National Park,
USA', *Canadian Journal of Zoology* 79, 2001, pp. 1401–9.

58 'quite a good thing, ecologically': Justin P. Suraci, Michael
Clinchy, Lawrence M. Dill, Devin Roberts and Liana Y. Zanette,
'Fear of large carnivores causes a trophic cascade', *Nature
Communications* 7, 2016, 10698, https://doi.org/10.1038/
ncomms10698.

58 'shown very neatly in a study of four sites': A. R. Hof,
J. Snellenberg and P. W. Bright, 'Food or fear? Predation risk
mediates edge refuging in an insectivorous mammal', *Animal
Behaviour* 83, 2012, pp. 1099–1106.

60 '50–90 per cent of their diet': P. Lüps, T. J. Roper and
G. Stocker, 'Stomach contents of badgers (*Meles meles L.*) in central
Switzerland', *Mammalia* 51, 1987, pp. 559–70; J. Goszczyński,
B. Jedrzejewska and W. Jedrzejewski, 'Diet composition of badgers
(*Meles meles*) in a pristine forest and rural habitats of Poland
compared to other European populations', *Journal of Zoology* 250,
2000, pp. 495–505.

60 'an average adult weight of 11–12 kilos': D. W. Macdonald and
P. Barrett, *Mammals of Britain and Europe*, Collins Field Guide, 5th
edn (Collins, 1993), p. 128.

61 'with increasing distance from the nearest badgers': T. Micol,
C. P. Doncaster and L. A. Mackinlay, 'Correlates of local variation in
the abundance of hedgehogs (*Erinaceus europaeus*)', *Journal of
Animal Ecology* 63, 1994, pp. 851–60.

61–2 'appears to be inversely correlated on farmland': R. P.
Young, J. Davison, I. D. Trewby, G. J. Wilson, R. J. Delahay and C. P.
Doncaster, 'Abundance of hedgehogs (*Erinaceus europaeus*) in
relation to the density and distribution of badgers (*Meles meles*)',
Journal of Zoology 269, 2006, pp. 349–56; B. M. Williams, P. J.
Baker, E. Thomas, G. Wilson, J. Judge and R. W. Yarnell, 'Reduced
occupancy of hedgehogs (*Erinaceus europaeus*) in rural England and
Wales: the influence of habitat and an asymmetric intra-guild
predator', *Scientific Reports* 8, 2018, pp. 1–10.

62 'far more likely to have hedgehogs': A. R. Hof and P. W. Bright, 'Factors affecting hedgehog presence on farmland as assessed by a questionnaire survey', *Acta Theriologica* 57, 2012, pp. 79–88.

62 'hedgehogs tended to be wherever badgers weren't': A. R. Hof, A. M. Allen and P. W. Bright, 'Investigating the role of the Eurasian badger (*Meles meles*) in the nationwide distribution of the western European hedgehog (*Erinaceus europaeus*) in England', *Animals* 9, 2019, p. 759.

62 'legal protection in the 1970s and 1990s': P. Cresswell, S. Harris and D. J. Jefferies, *The history, distribution, status and habitat requirements of the badger in Britain* (Nature Conservancy Council, 1990).

63 'social groups recorded in England had approximately doubled': Johanna Judge, Gavin J. Wilson, Roy Macarthur, Richard J. Delahay and Robbie A. McDonald, 'Density and abundance of badger social groups in England and Wales in 2011–2013', *Scientific Reports* 4, 2014, https://doi.org/10.1038/srep03809.

70 'total number killed at the time of writing is 143,241': https://www.badgertrust.org.uk/cull.

70 'up to a maximum of 75,930': https://www.gov.uk/government/publications/bovine-tb-authorisation-for-badger-control-in-2021.

71 'only 3–21 per cent in herd breakdowns': For a detailed account, see D. W. Macdonald, R. Woodroffe and P. Riordan, 'Badgers and bovine tuberculosis: beyond perturbation to life cycle analysis', in D. W. Macdonald and R. Feber, eds, *Wildlife conservation on farmland*, vol. 2: *Conflict in the countryside* (Oxford University Press, 2015), pp. 96–125.

72 '"the control of cattle TB in Britain"': http://www.bovinetb. info/docs/final_report.pdf.

72–3 '39 per cent overestimate of a population': D. W. Macdonald et al., 'Badgers and bovine tuberculosis', p. 115.

73 'only been doing it there for two years': S. H. Downs, A. Prosser, A. Ashton, S. Ashfield, L. A. Brunton, A. Brouwer and J. E. Parry, 'Assessing effects from four years of industry-led badger culling in England on the incidence of bovine tuberculosis in cattle, 2013–2017', *Scientific Reports* 9, 2019, pp. 1–14.

73 'rates of TB in cattle declined dramatically': https://www. badgertrust.org.uk/badger-cull-facts.

73 'between 10 and 20 per cent of TB cases': S. W. Martin, J. A. Eves, L.A. Dolan, R. F. Hammond, J. M. Griffin, J. D. Collins, and M. M. Shoukri, 'The association between the bovine tuberculosis status of herds in the East Offaly Project Area, and the distance to badger setts, 1988–1993', *Preventive Veterinary Medicine* 31, 1997, pp. 113–25.

74 'a figure of around 6 per cent': C. A. Donnelly and P. Nouvellet, 'The contribution of badgers to confirmed tuberculosis in cattle in high-incidence areas in England', *PLoS Currents*, 2013, https://doi.org/10.1371/currents.outbreaks.097a904d 3f3619db2fe78d24bc776098.

74 'only three (less than 1 per cent) had it': I. McGill, M. Jones, J. Goodall, R. Munro, A. Simmons, C. Packham, A. MacMillan, A. Knight, D. Dyer, C. Cheeseman and A. Grogan, 'Open letter to the prime minister regarding badger cull licences', *Veterinary Record* 187, 2020, e37.

74 'or indeed other badgers': https://www.badgertrust.org.uk/badger-cull-facts.

74 'in the implementation of biosecurity': Downs et al., 'Assessing effects from four years of industry-led badger culling in England', p. 11.

75 '"which has no basis in science"': Philip Case, 'Exclusive: *Farmers Weekly* spends a night on the badger cull', *Farmers Weekly*, 26 Sept. 2019, https://www.fwi.co.uk/livestock/health-welfare/livestock-diseases/bovine-tb/a-night-on-the-badger-cull-with-farmers.

75 'is proving tricky': Clare H. Benton, Jess Phoenix, Freya A. P. Smith, Andrew Robertson, Robbie A. McDonald, Gavin Wilson and Richard J. Delahay, 'Badger vaccination in England: progress, operational effectiveness and participant motivations', *People and Nature* 2, 2020, pp. 761–75.

75 'freely mixing with their herdmates': Iain McGill and Mark Jones, 'Cattle infectivity is driving the bTB epidemic', *Veterinary Record* 185 (22), 2019, pp. 699–700.

78 'make a mess of an unsuspecting badger': *Pilot badger culls in Somerset and Gloucestershire: report by the independent expert panel, chair: Professor Ranald Munro*, March 2014, https://assets.

publishing.service.gov.uk/government/uploads/system/uploads/
attachment_data/file/300382/independent-expert-panel-report.pdf.

78 ' "the potential for suffering that these figures imply" ': *Pilot badger culls in Somerset and Gloucestershire*, p. 50.

79 'measures that might actually solve the issue': Charles Godfray, Christl Donnelly, Glyn Hewinson, Michael Winter and James Wood, *Bovine TB strategy review: report to Rt Hon. Michael Gove MP, Secretary of State, DEFRA*, 2018, p. 1.

80 '12 hedgehogs over the entire experiment': Iain D. Trewby, Richard Young, Robbie A. McDonald, Gavin J. Wilson, John Davison, Neil Walker, Andrew Robertson, C. Patrick Doncaster and Richard J. Delahay, 'Impacts of removing badgers on localised counts of hedgehogs', *PLoS One* 9, 2014, e95477.

82 'just under half of those (49 per cent)': Ben M. Williams, Philip J. Baker, Emily Thomas, Gavin Wilson, Johanna Judge, and Richard W. Yarnell, 'Reduced occupancy of hedgehogs (Erinaceus europaeus) in rural England and Wales: The influence of habitat and an asymmetric intra-guild predator', *Scientific Reports* 8, 2018, pp. 1–10.

82 'a proxy for badger abundance': Micol et al. 1994; Young et al. 2006; Williams et al. 2018: cited in Lee, *Untangling the roles of prey availability, habitat quality and predation as predictors of hedgehog abundance*, p. 181.

82 'can vary between three and eight': J. Judge, G. Wilson, R. Macarthur, R. A. McDonald and R. J. Delahay, 'Abundance of badgers (*Meles meles*) in England and Wales', *Scientific Reports* 7, 2017, pp. 1–8.

82 'fifteen badgers or more per square kilometre': Lee,
Untangling the roles of prey availability, habitat quality and predation as predictors of hedgehog abundance, p. 181.

CHAPTER 4: COMING A CROPPER (BUT
PLOUGHING ON REGARDLESS)

93 'It isn't a clever joke': http://news.bbc.co.uk/1/hi/scotland/
edinburgh_and_east/8216991.stm.

**93 'excellent environments for hedgehog-munchable
invertebrates':** S. R. Amy, M. S. Heard, S. E. Hartley, C. T.
George, R. F. Pywell and J. T. Staley, 'Hedgerow rejuvenation
management affects invertebrate communities through changes
to habitat structure', *Basic and Applied Ecology* 16, 2015, pp.
443–51.

93 'some great hedgehog nesting sites': Pat Morris, *Hedgehogs*,
Whittet Books, new edn, 2015, p. 94.

94 'keeping up those all-important invertebrate numbers':
T. Merckx, L. Marini, R. E. Feber and D. W. Macdonald, 'Hedgerow
trees and extended-width field margins enhance macro-moth
diversity: implications for management', *Journal of Applied Ecology*
49, 2012, pp. 1396–1404.

94 'especially when dispersing': C. P. Doncaster, R. Carlo and
P. C. D. Johnson 'Field test for environmental correlates of dispersal
in hedgehogs *Erinaceus europaeus*', *Journal of Animal Ecology* 70,
2001, pp. 33–46.

94 '11.4°C in the hedgerows': C. E. Pettett, P. J. Johnson, T. P. Moorhouse, C. Hambly, J. R. Speakman and D. W. Macdonald, 'Daily energy expenditure in the face of predation: hedgehog energetics in rural landscapes', *Journal of Experimental Biology* 220, 2017, pp. 460–8.

94 'away from predation by badgers and foxes': A. R. Hof, J. Snellenberg and P. W. Bright, 'Food or fear? Predation risk mediates edge refuging in an insectivorous mammal', *Animal Behaviour* 83, 2012, pp. 1099–1106.

95 'lots of flora and fauna live in them': T. Cornulier, R. A. Robinson, D. Elston, X. Lambin, W. J. Sutherland and T. G. Benton, 'Bayesian reconstitution of environmental change from disparate historical records: hedgerow loss and farmland bird declines', *Methods in Ecology and Evolution* 2, 2011, pp. 86–94.

95 'need them to connect habitat patches together': D. W. Macdonald and P. J. Johnson, 'Farmers and the custody of the countryside: trends in loss and conservation of non-productive habitats 1981–1998', *Biological Conservation* 94, 2000, pp. 221–34.

95 'mobile species that use them as highways': M. Baguette, S. Blanchet, D. Legrand, V. M. Stevens and C. Turlure, 'Individual dispersal, landscape connectivity and ecological networks', *Biological Reviews* 88, 2013, pp. 310–26; A. Janin, J.-P. Léna, N. Ray, C. Delacourt, P. Allemand and P. Joly, 'Assessing landscape connectivity with calibrated cost–distance modelling: predicting common toad distribution in a context of spreading agriculture', *Journal of Applied Ecology* 46, 2009, pp. 833–41; Z. Zhang and M. B.

Usher, 'Dispersal of wood mice and bank voles in an agricultural landscape', *Acta Theriologica* 36, 1991, pp. 239–45.

95 **'the more extensive the surrounding hedgerow'**: S. D. Fitzgibbon, 'Small mammals in farm woodlands: the effect of habitat, isolation and surrounding land use patterns', *Journal of Applied Ecology* 34, 1997, pp. 530–9.

95 **'Both species use hedges to disperse'**: M. Gelling, D. W. Macdonald and F. Mathews, 'Are hedgerows the route to increased farmland small mammal density? Use of hedgerows in British pastoral habitats', *Landscape Ecology* 22, 2007, pp. 1019–32; Zhang and Usher, 'Dispersal of wood mice and bank voles in an agricultural landscape'.

95–6 **'when there are proportionally more crops'**: Janin et al., 'Assessing landscape connectivity with calibrated cost-distance modelling'.

96 **'linear features (i.e. hedges and tree lines) you have in a landscape'**: B. Verboom and H. Huitema, 'The importance of linear landscape elements for the pipistrelle *Pipistrellus pipistrellus* and the serotine bat *Eptesicus serotinus*', *Landscape Ecology* 12, 1997, pp. 117–25.

96 **'total length of British hedgerow from the 1940s vary'**: R. A. Robinson and W. J. Sutherland, 'Post-war changes in arable farming and biodiversity in Great Britain', *Journal of Applied Ecology* 39, 2002, pp. 157–76.

96 **'something like one million kilometres of them'**: Thomas Cornulier, Robert A. Robinson, David Elston, Xavier Lambin, William J. Sutherland, and Tim G. Benton, 'Bayesian reconstitution

of environmental change from disparate historical records: hedgerow loss and farmland bird declines', *Methods in Ecology and Evolution*, 2, 2011, pp. 86–94.

97 'pretty much stayed around that figure since': P. D. Carey, S. M. Wallis, B. Emmett, L. C. Maskell, J. Murphy, L. R. Norton, L. C. Simpson and S. M. Smart, *Countryside Survey: UK headline messages from 2007* (Centre for Ecology and Hydrology, 2008), https://nora.nerc.ac.uk/id/eprint/4986/1/N004986BK.pdf.

97 '(22 per cent of the then-existing hedgerow stock) was grubbed out': C. Barr, D. Howard, B. Bunce, M. Gillespie and C. Hallam, *Changes in hedgerows in Britain between 1984 and 1990*, report produced under contract to the Department of the Environment (Institute of Terrestrial Ecology, 1991), https://nora.nerc.ac.uk/id/eprint/4624/1/N004624CR.pdf.

97 'before they got prevented by any new legislation': Geoffrey Lean, 'The hedgerow: 8,000 miles vanish each year', *Independent*, 26 Oct. 1996, https://www.independent.co.uk/news/uk/home-news/the-hedgerow-8-000-miles-vanish-each-year-1360413.html.

97 'if you could stack all the planets of the solar system': https://www.universetoday.com/115672/you-could-fit-all-the-planets-between-the-earth-and-the-moon/.

98 'less than 0.25 per cent of the crop gets left behind': Robinson and Sutherland, 'Post-war changes in arable farming and biodiversity in Great Britain'.

98 'a third of those found in pastoral counties': Robinson and Sutherland, 'Post-war changes in arable farming and biodiversity in Great Britain'.

99 'only 31 per cent of hedgerows are well managed': Carey et al., *Countryside Survey*, p. 16.

99 'three million hectares by the year 2000': Robinson and Sutherland, 'Post-war changes in arable farming and biodiversity in Great Britain'.

100 'the loss of invertebrates is heavily implicated': D. E. Chamberlain, R. J. Fuller, G. H. Bunce, J. C. Duckworth and M. Shrubb, 'Changes in the abundance of farmland birds in relation to the timing of agricultural intensification in England and Wales', *Journal of Applied Ecology* 37, 2000, pp. 771–88.

100 'fifteen species (of eighteen studied) declined in abundance': R. J. Fuller, R. D. Gregory, D. W. Gibbons, J. H. Marchant, J. D. Wilson and N. Carter, 'Population declines and range contractions among lowland farmland birds in Britain', *Conservation Biology* 9, 1995, pp. 1425–41.

100 'approximately halved between 1968 and 1995': G. M. Siriwardena, S. R. Baillie, S. T. Buckland, R. M. Fewster, J. H. Marchant and J. D. Wilson, 'Trends in abundance of farmland birds: a quantitative comparison of smoothed Common Birds Census indices', *Journal of Applied Ecology* 35, 1998, pp. 24–43.

100 'for both insects and spiders': T. G. Benton, D. M. Bryant, L. Cole and H. Q. Crick, 'Linking agricultural practice to insect and bird populations: a historical study over three decades', *Journal of Applied Ecology* 39, 2002, pp. 673–87.

100 'those practices' effects on farmland invertebrates': Benton et al., 'Linking agricultural practice to insect and bird populations'.

100–101 'lower invertebrate and plant food resources': P. W. Atkinson, R. J. Fuller and J. A. Vickery, 'Large-scale patterns of summer and winter bird distribution in relation to farmland type in England and Wales', *Ecography* 25, 2002, pp. 466–80, https://doi.org/10.1034/j.1600-0587.2002.250409.x.

101 'a lack of alternative grasslands and woodlands to forage in': W. J. Peach, M. Denny, P. A. Cotton, I. F. Hill, D. Gruar, D. Barritt, A. Impey and J. Mallord, 'Habitat selection by song thrushes in stable and declining farmland populations', *Journal of Applied Ecology* 41, 2004, pp. 275–93, https://doi.org/10.1111/j.0021-8901.2004.00892.x.

101 'a sustained loss of farmland biodiversity': T. G. Benton, J. A. Vickery and J. D. Wilson, 'Farmland biodiversity: is habitat heterogeneity the key?', *Trends in Ecology and Evolution* 18, 2003, pp. 182–8, https://doi.org/10.1016/S0169-5347(03)00011-9; M. Emmerson, M. B. Morales, J. J. Oñate, P. Batáry, F. Berendse, J. Liira, T. Aavik, I. Guerrero, R. Bommarco, S. Eggers, T. Pärt, T. Tscharntkes, W. Weisser, L. Clement and J. Bengtsson, 'How agricultural intensification affects biodiversity and ecosystem services', *Advances in Ecological Research* 55, 2016, pp. 43–97, https://doi.org/10.1016/BS.AECR.2016.08.005.

102 'rising to 62 per cent in the second': Macdonald and Johnson, 'Farmers and the custody of the countryside'.

104 'ultimately ran counter to their values': Macdonald and Johnson, 'Farmers and the custody of the countryside'.

105 'a sign of a "good" farmer': C. Young, C. Morris and C. Andrews, 'Agriculture and the environment in the UK:

towards an understanding of "farming culture" ', *Greener Environment International* 12, 1995, pp. 63–80; R. J. Burton, 'Understanding farmers' aesthetic preference for tidy agricultural landscapes: a Bourdieusian perspective', *Landscape Research* 37, 2012, pp. 51–71.

105 'a good reason for removing hedgerows': Macdonald and Johnson, 'Farmers and the custody of the countryside'.

105 'also a farmer's social position': Burton, 'Understanding farmers' aesthetic preference for tidy agricultural landscapes'.

111 'four and eight hedgehogs respectively': P. A. Morris, S. Munn and S. Craig-Wood, 'The effects of releasing captive hedgehogs (*Erinaceus europaeus*) into the wild', *Field Studies* 8, 1992, pp. 89–99; P. A. Morris, K. Meakin and S. Sharafi, 'The behaviour and survival of rehabilitated hedgehogs (*Erinaceus europaeus*)', *Animal Welfare* 2, 1993, pp. 53–66.

111–12 'on to a pasture farm in Devon': P. A. Morris and H. Warwick, 'A study of rehabilitated juvenile hedgehogs after release into the wild', *Animal Welfare* 3, 1994, pp. 163–77.

112 'rarely using any of the cropped fields': P. A. Morris, 'Released, rehabilitated hedgehogs: a follow-up study in Jersey', *Animal Welfare* 6, 1997, pp. 317–27.

115 'a hedgehog may seek somewhere calmer': C. P. Doncaster, 'Factors regulating local variations in abundance: field tests on hedgehogs, *Erinaceus europaeus*', *Oikos* 69, 1995, pp. 182–92.

120 'last of all (you guessed it), arable land': K. A. Lee, *Untangling the roles of prey availability, habitat quality and predation as* *predictors of hedgehog abundance*, PhD dissertation, Nottingham Trent University, 2021, p. 80.

120 'soil compaction from heavy modern machinery':
T. Decaëns and J. J. Jiménez, 'Earthworm communities under an agricultural intensification gradient in Colombia', *Plant and Soil* 240, 2002, pp. 133–43.

121 'hedgehogs foraged less in response to badger odour': J. F. Ward, D. W. Macdonald and C. P. Doncaster, 'Responses of foraging hedgehogs to badger odour', *Animal Behaviour* 53, 1997, pp. 709–20.

125 'towards becoming an exclusively urban species': J. L. van de Poel, J. Dekker and F. van Langevelde, 'Dutch hedgehogs *Erinaceus europaeus* are nowadays mainly found in urban areas, possibly due to the negative effects of badgers *Meles meles*', *Wildlife Biology* 21, 2015, pp. 51–5.

CHAPTER 5: AN ENGLISHMAN'S HOME IS A CASTLE (UNFORTUNATELY)

131 'predicted to reach US$3.9 billion by 2027': https://www.arizton.com/market-reports/robotic-lawn-mower-market-2023.

133 'only one model passed all ten tests': S. L. Rasmussen, A. E. Schrøder, R. Mathiesen, J. L. Nielsen, C. Pertoldi and D. W. Macdonald, 'Wildlife conservation at a garden level: the effect of robotic lawn mowers on European hedgehogs (*Erinaceus europaeus*)', *Animals* 11, 2021, 1191, https://doi.org/10.3390/ani11051191.

134 'Sophie's research on the subject': Sophie Lund Rasmussen, 'Do robotic lawnmowers hurt hedgehogs? Dr Hedgehog has the answer', *ScienceNordic*, 8 May 2021, https://sciencenordic.com/animals-denmark/do-robotic-lawn-mowers-hurt-hedgehogs-dr-hedgehog-has-the-answer/1856882.

137 'slowly constrict and embed as the hedgehog grows': Andrew Ellson, 'Postmen's rubber bands rebound on hedgehogs', *The Times*, 15 Dec. 2015, https://www.thetimes.co.uk/article/postmens-rubber-bands-rebound-on-hedgehogs-wsw8sjh2mx8; Chad Nugent, 'Posties dumping their elastic bands are a danger to hedgehogs', *Daily Gazette/Essex County Standard*, 21 May 2019, https://www.gazette-news.co.uk/news/17647809.posties-dumping-elastic-bands-danger-hedgehogs/; 'Girl, seven, sends letter reprimanding Royal Mail staff over dumped rubber bands', *Belfast Telegraph*, 28 Feb. 2018, https://www.belfasttelegraph.co.uk/news/viral/girl-seven-sends-letter-reprimanding-royal-mail-staff-over-dumped-rubber-bands-36655787.html.

137 'versus the background average of light intensity': A. Berger, B. Lozano, L. M. Barthel and N. Schubert, 'Moving in the dark – evidence for an influence of artificial light at night on the movement behaviour of European hedgehogs (*Erinaceus europaeus*)', *Animals* 10, 2020, p. 1306.

138 'heading to their usual foraging grounds': A. Berger, L. M. Barthel, W. Rast, H. Hofer and P. Gras, 'Urban hedgehog behavioural responses to temporary habitat disturbance versus permanent fragmentation', *Animals* 10, 2020, p. 2109.

140 'urban areas (most often gardens)': D. Wembridge, G. Johnson, N. Al-Fulaij and S. Langton, *The state of Britain's hedgehogs 2022* (People's Trust for Endangered Species, 2022), p. 3.

143 'to 19 per square kilometre': A. L. Taucher, S. Gloor, A. Dietrich, M. Geiger, D. Hegglin and F. Bontadina, 'Decline in distribution and abundance: urban hedgehogs under pressure', *Animals* 10, 2020, p. 1606.

148 'gardens (which comprise about half a city's green space)': Ken Thompson and Steve Head, 'Gardens as a resource for wildlife', *Wildlife Gardening Forum*, n.d., http://www.wlgf.org/The%20 garden%20Resource.pdf.

148 'a total area of 4,330 km²': Z. G. Davies, R. A. Fuller, A. Loram, K. N. Irvine, V. Sims and K. J. Gaston, 'A national scale inventory of resource provision for biodiversity within domestic gardens', *Biological Conservation* 142, 2009, pp. 761–71.

148 'something like 39,000–139,000 hedgehogs': From densities on p. 17 of T. P. Moorhouse, *Population viability analysis of hedgehogs in rural and urban habitats*, report prepared for the People's Trust for Endangered Species, 2013.

156 'those of other people they had persuaded': A. Gazzard, A. Boushall, E. Brand and P. J. Baker, 'An assessment of a conservation strategy to increase garden connectivity for hedgehogs that requires cooperation between immediate neighbours: a barrier too far?' *PLoS One* 16, 2021, e0259537, https://doi.org/10.1371/ journal.pone.0259537.

157 '**(51 per cent, 16 per cent and 21 per cent, respectively)**': Davies et al., 'A national scale inventory of resource provision for biodiversity within domestic gardens'.

161 '**taking in a few other sights en route**': P. A. Morris, 'The effects of supplementary feeding on movements of hedgehogs (*Erinaceus europaeus*)', *Mammal Review* 15, 1985, pp. 23–33.

162 '**versus 34 per cent where they have not**': A. Gazzard and P. J. Baker, 'Patterns of feeding by householders affect activity of hedgehogs (*Erinaceus europaeus*) during the hibernation period', *Animals* 10, 2020, p. 1344.

162 '**and/or where there is a compost heap**': A. Gazzard, R. W. Yarnell and P. J. Baker, 'Fine-scale habitat selection of a small mammalian urban adapter: the West European hedgehog (*Erinaceus europaeus*)', *Mammalian Biology* 102, 2022, pp. 1–17.

163 '**gardens that surrounded the one offering food**': S. L. Rasmussen, T. B. Berg, T. Dabelsteen and O. R. Jones, 'The ecology of suburban juvenile European hedgehogs (*Erinaceus europaeus*) in Denmark', *Ecology and Evolution* 9, 2019, pp. 13174–87, https://doi.org/10.1002/ece3.5764.

CHAPTER 6: A MURDERER UNMASKED

178 '**in Kent in 2019 and nationwide in 2021**': L. Ball, R. Still, A. Riggs, A. Skilbeck, M. Shardlow, A. Whitehouse and P. Tinsley-Marshall, *The Bugs Matter Citizen Science Survey: counting insect 'splats' on vehicle number plates*, technical report by Buglife and Royal Society for the Protection of Birds (Policy Commons, 2022), https://policycommons.net/artifacts/2390158/bugs-matter-2021-national-report/3411374/.

179 'declined by three-quarters in under thirty years': Caspar A. Hallmann, Martin Sorg, Eelke Jongejans, Henk Siepel, Nick Hofland, Heinz Schwan, Werner Stenmans, Andreas Müller, Hubert Sumser, Thomas Hörren, Dave Goulson and Hans de Kroon, 'More than 75 percent decline over 27 years in total flying insect biomass in protected areas', *PLoS One* 12, 2017, e0185809, https://doi.org/10.1371/journal.pone.0185809.

179 'pretty well predicted by their biomass': C. A. Hallmann, A. Ssymank, M. Sorg, H. de Kroon and E. Jongejans, 'Insect biomass decline scaled to species diversity: general patterns derived from a hoverfly community', *Proceedings of the National Academy of Sciences* 118 (2), 2021, https://www.pnas.org/doi/10.1073/pnas.2002554117.

180 ' "a third are being threatened with extinction" ': F. Sánchez-Bayo and K. A. Wyckhuys, 'Worldwide decline of the entomofauna: a review of its drivers', *Biological Conservation* 232, 2019, pp. 8–27.

181 'spiralling downward at an alarming rate': R. Inger, R. Gregory, J. P. Duffy, I. Stott, P. Voříšek and K. J. Gaston, 'Common European birds are declining rapidly while less abundant species' numbers are rising', *Ecology Letters* 18, 2015, pp. 28–36.

182 'Rare species can buck a general trend': Inger et al., 'Common European birds are declining rapidly while less abundant species' numbers are rising'.

182 'sucking the life out of the reserves': Hallmann et al., 'More than 75 percent decline over 27 years in total flying insect biomass in protected areas'.

182 'pesticide use in both breeding and wintering areas': R. L. Stanton, C. A. Morrissey and R. G. Clark, 'Analysis of trends and agricultural drivers of farmland bird declines in North America: a review', *Agriculture, Ecosystems and Environment* 254, 2018, pp. 244–54.

183 'the various conservation ills that had befallen them': S. L. Maxwell, R. A. Fuller, T. M. Brooks and J. E. Watson, 'Biodiversity: the ravages of guns, nets and bulldozers', *Nature* 536, 2016, pp. 143–5.

183 'birds, mammals and amphibians': Sean L. Maxwell, Richard A. Fuller, Thomas M. Brooks and James E. M. Watson, 'Supplementary information to: The ravages of guns, nets and bulldozers (Comment in *Nature* 536, 143–5, 2016)', 11 Aug. 2016, https://static-content.springer.com/esm/art%3A10.1038% 2F536143a/MediaObjects/41586_2016_BF536143a_MOESM1_ ESM.pdf.

184 'overexploitation, agricultural activity, or a combination of both': Maxwell et al., 'Supplementary information'; C. Bellard, P. Cassey and T. M. Blackburn, 'Alien species as a driver of recent extinctions', *Biology Letters* 12, 2016, 20150623.

184 'more than doubled between 1961 and 2016': 'Land use in agriculture by the numbers', Food and Agriculture Organization of the United Nations, 7 May 2020, https://www.fao.org/sustainability/ news/detail/en/c/1274219/.

184 'for the production of food, feed and energy is still increasing': T. Newbold, L. N. Hudson, S. L. Hill, S. Contu, I. Lysenko, R. A. Senior, L. Börger, D. J. Bennett, A, Choimes, B. Collen and J. Day, 'Global effects of land use on local terrestrial biodiversity', *Nature* 520, 2015, pp. 45–50; D. Tilman, Michael Clark, David R. Williams, Kaitlin Kimmel, Stephen Polasky and Craig Packer, 'Future threats to biodiversity and pathways to their prevention', *Nature* 546, 2017, pp. 73–81.

185 'around a fifth of a hectare each now': 'Land use in agriculture by the numbers', Food and Agriculture Organization.

185 'Very little unused fertile land is left': E. C. Ellis, J. O. Kaplan, D. O. Fuller, S. Vavrus, K. Klein Goldewijk and P. H. Verburg, 'Used planet: a global history', *Proceedings of the National Academy of Sciences* 110, 2013, pp. 7978–85; H. Haberl, 'Competition for land: a sociometabolic perspective', *Ecological Economics* 119, 2015, pp. 424–31.

185 'to rely heavily on agricultural intensification': Tilman et al., 'Future threats to biodiversity and pathways to their prevention'.

185 'the *intensity* of agriculture is a matter of life and death': Philipp Semenchuk, Christoph Plutzar, Thomas Kastner, Sarah Matej, Giorgio Bidoglio, Karl-Heinz Erb, Franz Essl, Helmut Haberl, Johannes Wessely, Fridolin Krausmann and Stefan Dullinger, 'Relative effects of land conversion and land-use intensity on terrestrial vertebrate diversity', *Nature Communications* 13, 2022, pp. 1–10.

185 'still used at low intensity': B. E. Graeub, M. J. Chappell, H. Wittman, S. Ledermann, R. B. Kerr and B. Gemmill-Herren, 'The state of family farms in the world', *World Development* 87, 2016, pp. 1–15.

185 'rotated crop plants and low-density herds': M. Beckmann, K. Gerstner, M. Akin-Fajiye, S. Ceauşu, S. Kambach, N. L. Kinlock, H. R. Phillips, W. Verhagen, J. Gurevitch, S. Klotz and T. Newbold, 'Conventional land-use intensification reduces species richness and increases production: a global meta-analysis', *Global Change Biology* 25, 2019, pp. 1941–56.

186 'high grazing pressure': Beckmann et al., 'Conventional land-use intensification reduces species richness and increases production'.

186 'increases yields by around 85 per cent': Beckmann et al., 'Conventional land-use intensification reduces species richness and increases production'.

186 'current rates of loss of vertebrate biodiversity globally': Semenchuk et al., 'Relative effects of land conversion and land-use intensity on terrestrial vertebrate diversity'.

186 'a global food crisis': Michael Le Page, 'Global food crisis is leaving millions hungry, but there are solutions', *New Scientist*, 23 May 2022, https://www.newscientist.com/article/2321492-global-food-crisis-is-leaving-millions-hungry-but-there-are-solutions/.

187 'half of the surface of the Earth back to nature': Z. Mehrabi, E. C. Ellis and N. Ramankutty, N. 'The challenge of feeding the world while conserving half the planet', *Nature Sustainability* 1, 2018, pp. 409–12.

188 '3 per cent of food calories': Mehrabi et al., 'The challenge of feeding the world while conserving half the planet'.

188 'substantial drops in available food': FAOSTAT (Food and Agriculture Organization of the United Nations, 2016), http://www.fao.org/faostat/en/.

188–9 'feed humans and save wildlife': David Leclère, Michael Obersteiner, Mike Barrett, Stuart H. M. Butchart, Abhishek Chaudhary, Adriana de Palma and A. J. Fabrice, 'Bending the curve of terrestrial biodiversity needs: an integrated strategy', *Nature* 585, 2020, pp. 551–6.

189 'to preserve flourishing populations of wildlife': Leclère et al., 'Bending the curve of terrestrial biodiversity needs'.

190 'reduction in deforestation and carbon emissions': Florian Humpenöder, Benjamin Leon Bodirsky, Isabelle Weindl, Hermann Lotze-Campen, Tomas Linder and Alexander Popp, 'Projected environmental benefits of replacing beef with microbial protein', *Nature* 605, 2022, pp. 90–6, https://doi.org/10.1038/s41586-022-04629-w.

190 'working together for the EAT-Lancet Commission': Kerry Torrens, 'What is the planetary health diet?', BBC Good Food, n.d., https://www.bbcgoodfood.com/howto/guide/what-is-the-planetary-health-diet; 'The planetary health diet', EAT-Lancet Commission, n.d., https://eatforum.org/eat-lancet-commission/the-planetary-health-diet-and-you/.

191 'the country's food consumption': Q. D. Read, K. L. Hondula and M. K. Muth, 'Biodiversity effects of food system sustainability: actions from farm to fork', *Proceedings of the National Academy of Sciences* 119, 2022, e2113884119.

193 'keeping conservation efforts from conflicting with food security': Leclère et al., 'Bending the curve of terrestrial biodiversity needs'.

197 'compared with the least intensive urban sites': J. Millard, C. L. Outhwaite, R. Kinnersley, R. Freeman, R. D. Gregory, O. Adedoja, S. Gavini, E. Kioko, M. Kuhlmann, J. Ollerton and Z. X. Ren, 'Global effects of land-use intensity on local pollinator biodiversity', *Nature Communications* 12, 2021, pp. 1–11.

198 'It costs money, creates rather than saves work': See https://www.jackwallington.com/17-reasons-to-avoid-fake-lawns-how-bad-is-artificial-grass-for-the-environment/.

199 'the campaign run by Plantlife': Helena Horton, 'Mow problem: gardeners encouraged not to cut lawns in May', *Guardian*, 29 April 2022, https://www.theguardian.com/environment/2022/apr/29/no-mow-may-gardeners-not-to-cut-lawns-wild-plants-insects?CMP=Share_AndroidApp_Other.

205 'telling them why the holes were so important': 'The hedgehog highwayman', *FOLKFeatures*, 1 Sept. 2020, https://folkfeatures.co.uk/the-hedgehog-highwayman-2/.

205 'rubber bands should be kept for re-use': 'Girl, seven, sends letter reprimanding Royal Mail staff over dumped rubber bands', *Belfast Telegraph*, 28 Feb. 2018, https://www.belfasttelegraph.co.uk/

news/viral/girl-seven-sends-letter-reprimanding-royal-mail-staff-over-dumped-rubber-bands-36655787.html.

206 'the most hazardous types of pesticides': Arthur Neslen, 'European fruit with traces of most toxic pesticides "up 53% in nine years"', *Guardian*, 24 May 2022, https://www.theguardian.com/environment/2022/may/24/european-fruit-with-traces-of-most-toxic-pesticides-up-53-in-nine-years?CMP=Share_AndroidApp_Other

207 'upon which all human well-being depends': See Tom Moorhouse, *Elegy for a river: whiskers, claws and conservation's last, wild hope* (Doubleday, 2021).

ACKNOWLEDGEMENTS

This book exists due to the magnificence of a crack squad of experts. I owe a debt of gratitude to, in no particular order, Richard Yarnell, Phillip Baker, David Wembridge, Sophie Rasmussen, Lauren Moore, Carly Pettett, Abi Gazzard, Nida Al-Fulaij, Grace Johnson, Trevor Lawson, Mike Collard, Chris Sandom and Ruth Feber. They were fantastically generous with their time and expertise when it was far from obvious that I would make good use of either. And nobody has been more generous than Hugh Warwick. His passion and work for hedgehogs are legendary, and his book, *A Prickly Affair* (a hedgehog must-read) is a truly intimidating act to attempt to follow. I have greatly appreciated his support and guidance. Finally, where hedgehogs are concerned Pat Morris has been there, done that, invented the loom on which the T-shirt was woven and, of course, written the books. For the hedgehog completist, his *Hedgehog* in the New Naturalist series is rammed full of fascinating details. For older children and the casual hogger, *Hedgehogs* (Whittet Books) is excellent. That Pat took time out of what he claims to be his retirement (but which clearly isn't) to chat hedgehogs was wonderful.

Thank you all again.

INDEX

ABOUT THE AUTHOR

Dr Tom Moorhouse is a conservation research scientist who worked for over twenty years at the Wildlife Conservation Research Unit, part of Oxford University's Biology Department. Over his career he has researched quite a lot of British wildlife, most of which tried to bite him. The hedgehogs were an exception, and he is still grateful for their forbearance. Tom is the author of *Elegy for a River* as well as award-winning children's fiction. He lives with his wife and daughter in Oxford. One day he hopes to persuade wild hedgehogs back into his garden.